Outdoor
Performance
Cannabis

Outdoor
Performance
Cannabis

Dustin Fraser
With the help of Kyle L. Ladenburger

Published by High County Publishing, LLC

701 S. Carson St., Ste 200 | Carson City, NV 89701-5239 USA

www.highcountypublishing.com

Book design copyright © 2017 by High County Publishing, LLC

Published in the USA

ISBN: 978-0-9987782-0-4
1. Biography & Autobiography
2. Horticultural
3. Cannabis

Table of Contents

Forward

An introduction to Dustin Fraser

By Helene Isbell

Dustin Fraser is a true cannabis connoisseur and one of the great growers of California. He holds a deep appreciation for the plant and all it has to offer our society.

Growing up in the foothills of the Sierra Nevada Mountains, living on an agora goat farm in Tuolumne County, he developed a love of horticulture, agriculture, and the idea of growing or raising what you eat as much as possible.

As a young adult in Sonoma County, Dustin gained extensive experience in the technicalities of indoor growing, and all of its options to mimic nature. His experiments with hydroponic gardening achieved unprecedented yields.

But it was in 2006 when Dustin and his family moved to Covelo, California, a tiny town hidden deep in Mendocino County, that he began experimenting with what he would come to call Performance Cannabis .

By nature, cannabis is what horticulturists call an opportunistic plant, meaning it is genetically predisposed to maximize growth when conditions are perfect. In other words, those people who have claimed cannabis grows like a weed were on to something.

What if, Dustin reasoned, everything nutrients, moisture, temperature, plant structure could be controlled and made as perfect as possible? How large could the plant grow? How much could the yield be increased? *Could the weed grow into a tree?*

Growing outdoors in rural Mendocino County, Dustin has perfected his method of growing the cannabis plant into a tree, maximizing yield. His gardens are designed for performance. **Outdoor Performance Cannabis** explains his methods, experiences, trials, and errors.

In comparison to the cost of setting up a large greenhouse grow; *Dustin's method of turning cannabis plants into trees is exceedingly economical.* His yields are great. His experience and discussion of marketing the crop are invaluable.

Outdoor Performance Cannabis is easy to read and easy to follow. Dustin's system can be scaled to any size garden, from a few plants to hundreds. The container size, which will effect plant growth, can also be scaled from big to biggest, going from 100 gallon all the way up to 1,000-gallon containers.

A recognized innovator in growing cannabis, in 2007 Dustin Fraser was the first medicinal grower to discover and use Smart Pots, a soft-sided fabric aeration container. He came across the product while reading a California Nursery Association magazine, and immediately recognized the possibility that the Smart Pot might have a significant impact on the cannabis growing industry.

Dustin became an integral part of creating the Smart Pot brand. His concept was a game changer for both indoor and outdoor growers, greatly increasing yields and raising the level of horticultural knowledge throughout the grow industry. He became a recognized face of the company, traveling the globe and winning awards from Mendocino and the Emerald Triangle of California, to the whole of the USA and Canada, Europe, and Japan. His industry friends are many, from Holland, Spain, and Austria, to San Francisco and points north.

Dustin is a true horticulturist and do-it-yourself organic grower who has produced and sold compost teas, bulk fungus, beneficial bacteria, kelp, and humic acid. His homegrown tomatoes, asparagus, artichokes, and everything else green are legendary, especially when carefully prepared by his wife.

He has owned and operated two successful retail grow stores. In 2014 he became a founding member of Central Coast garden products, a California-based manufacturer and distributor of natural pest control products brand named Green Cleaner and Root Cleaner.

I am honored to be a partner in Dustin's most current project, High Country Genetics. One of Dustin's lifelong dreams has been to perfect and preserve the classic and exotic varieties that have come to characterize American strains of cannabis. High Country Genetics will collect and distribute some of the highest-grade medical cannabis in the industry.

Dustin's passion and respect for the cannabis plant has been a driving force behind his entrepreneurial spirit. He wants the healing properties of cannabis to be safely accessible to all who can enjoy its benefits. Great cannabis starts with great growing. I hope you enjoy **Outdoor Performance Cannabis**. With the recent changes in laws and attitudes, it is a new world for growers. The story is far from over - in fact, it has only just begun!

Chapter One

Beginnings

The Emerald Triangle is the nickname given to a region of Northwestern California and is comprised of three rural counties: Mendocino, Humbolt, and Trinity. These counties are arguably the epicenter for cannabis production in all of the United States and possibly the world. During the mid-1960s and early 1970s, waves of likeminded people flocked to these hills, mountains, and valleys to grow quality cannabis outdoors (at that time, illicitly). The vast amounts of rural land (combined, the counties span over 10,000 sq. mi.) coupled with long summers and a moderate climate make the Emerald Triangle an ideal location for outdoor cannabis production.

Since the approval of California Proposition 215 in 1996, which enacted the legalization of medicinal cannabis production and consumption, the area has further exploded with growers to fill the high demand. Though the population of the three counties (just above 230,000) is relatively low for the amount of area, growers annually produce large amounts of cannabis. Not only is cannabis a part of the Emerald Triangle culture, it is also a major source of income. It is commonly said that almost everyone in the Emerald Triangle is involved with the industry either directly or indirectly through other services and businesses that thrive due to the booming cannabis market.

The Emerald Triangle is where I developed and perfected my technique for growing cannabis outdoors, a system I call Performance Gardening. Traditionally, cannabis is grown either in the ground or in a greenhouse; I believe my methods are a great improvement on the old standards. In the Emerald Triangle, it is not uncommon to see cannabis plants tower up to eight feet. My plants consistently surpass 10 feet, are as big around as they are tall, and the buds have superior quality. The yields average over 10 pounds per plant (dry weight). My hope is that everyone can benefit from the knowledge I have gained, and achieve the satisfaction of a great harvest.

At face value a high performance outdoor cannabis garden is just an outdoor container garden for cannabis; however, when you examine the operation closely it is a finely-tuned machine that delivers stellar results almost every time. These methods allows plants to come closer to their full genetic potential than they would with any other growing system. Cannabis is what horticulturists call an opportunistic plant, meaning that genetically the plant is predisposed to absorb all the good things you might give it. By growing outside in large containers (from 200-1,000 gallons in size), specifically Smart Pot fabric aeration containers, the grower is able to control all of the components and inputs involved. This control can result in maximum growth and superior yields. In addition, the Performance Gardening method is completely scalable to any size grow operation, making it an ideal approach for any type of legal outdoor cannabis production.

This book details, by section, all of the steps it takes to grow a high performance outdoor cannabis garden, offering an in-depth view of the entire process from start to finish. From choosing a grow sight and establishing the garden, to proper irrigation and fertilization, and from starting plants, via seeds or clones, to

One of the many valleys nestled in the mountains of the beautiful and vast Emerald Triangle of Northern California

general plant care throughout all stages, I will get you started and get you thinking. There is also discussion on how to design an effective plant support/caging system to keep plants upright, as well as proper trellising of the flower-heavy branches. I move step by step through the entire season including harvesting, drying and curing the buds, as well as the when and how to market the end product more profitably. Information on how to stay in compliance with the state, county, and local laws is also included. This knowledge is important for every sustainable cannabis business.

Packed with pictures, diagrams, and pages of useful information, this book is meant to be a reference manual and not a coffee table decoration. It is a complete guide to growing a high performance cannabis garden. Much like a great cookbook that gets covered in flour and batter throughout the years, this book is meant to get dirty. So take it with you into the garden and don t be afraid to let it get dirty. The information you need to grow giant outdoor cannabis plants is now at your finger tips, so get out there and grow yourself some trees!

Chapter Two

Selecting a Grow Sight

Upon deliberation of where to start a high performance outdoor cannabis garden, the old familiar, worn-out adage still rings eternally clear: location, location, location. However, location in regards to selecting the perfect grow sight will encompass much more than whether the area has plentiful sun and water. There are several aspects that need to be taken into consideration ranging from environmental conditions to local regulations. The ultimate grow sight location should hinge on many factors including, but not limited to, the following.

Local Politics & Regulations:

When selecting the location of a high performance, outdoor cannabis garden it is of utmost importance to understand the rules and regulations in your area all the way up from the state level down to the county and city/township level. Furthermore, it is of equal importance to obtain the required licensing and permits to get the operation up and running, especially if you wish to do things in a sustainable and legal way. Laws and regulations can vary from town to town, and even from the county level to the towns within that county, so it is imperative to have a clear understanding of the local guidelines. For example, more densely populated places like suburban areas and towns might have certain regulations that can lead to stricter implementation with regard to neighborhoods, school zones, and other public places. Outdoor cannabis gardens are typically required to be out of the public sight, and following the rules will dramatically lower the grower's risk of getting into trouble. Generally, the proper way to go about selecting a high-performance cannabis gardening sight is to find an area with plenty of available space in which outdoor production has been a common part of the culture for many years, and where a larger number of grow sights are operational. Call it the "strength in numbers" approach. These kind of local environments, where seasonal cannabis production is both a part of the culture as well as the economy, are most often found in rural areas where populations and law enforcement presence alike are at lower levels.

Respect Thy Neighbor:

Keep in mind that we humans are a social creature and any place chosen for a growing sight, regardless of how remote it is, will still be part of a larger community and one will almost undoubtedly have neighbors to deal with at some point in time. So remember, respect given is often respect repaid. The more inviting and accepting an area is to outdoor cannabis cultivation the better, but there are still many people that draw a hard line of opposition to the practice regardless of the laws and regulations of their particular community. Keeping in complete legal compliance is the best way to traverse the situation. A high-performance outdoor cannabis garden is best left as far out of sight as possible and, in turn, out of the minds and concerns of any neighbors. By not allowing any sort of criminal element into the grow and by upholding the utmost respect and consideration for any and all neighbors, a grower will be free to go about daily business with very few troubles. A disgruntled or unhappy neighbor can result in complaints to local law enforcement, and as the complaints multiply the law enforcement body may be forced to take some sort of action.

Locating the performance garden in an area with as few neighbors as possible will result in less unforeseen hassles and stress.

Securing the Grow Sight:

A certain level of security protocol is a must when it comes to a high-performance outdoor cannabis garden. This type of endeavor is often the target of vandalism, destruction, or even outright theft. Cannabis is a highly lucrative crop and some people will try to illegally profit off the hard work of others. Tie this together with the fact that some people are against the practice in general and may try to physically damage or destroy the operation, therefore one can easily see the need for some preventative security measures. Lo-

A tall fence can help protect a performance garden hidden from unwanted viewers and also provide privacy when work is being done.

cating the grow sight so that it is out of sight and not visible from places like roads, other people's properties, and streams/rivers is the best first step to take.

Erecting a strong reliable fence is next. A proper fence will be made from wood or metal and should be tall enough to obstruct viewing of the garden from the outside. A tall fence also makes it harder for potential thieves and vandals to scale and create havoc inside. Equip the fence with a sturdy gate and a trusty lock and the external perimeter will be much more secure. The addition of dogs to a grow sight can also be helpful as dogs, especially in groups, will usually bark loudly and alert their owner of any potential intrusions. Guns, however, are not such a good idea and many county and local laws have provisions that make the addition of firearms to an outdoor cannabis garden sight cause enough to change a legal/permitted grow into a punishable felony.

Perhaps the most important thing someone can do when operating a functioning high-performance outdoor cannabis garden is to be humble and to not gloat or brag all over town. The more attention a grower draws to themselves the higher the potential of having serious security threats directed towards their gardens. By staying as far off, or under, the radar as possible, the likelihood of experiencing adverse problems can be drastically reduced.

Water Supply:

When it comes to a high-performance outdoor cannabis garden a consistent, reliable water source is a must. As the size of the plants increase, so will their ability to consume large amounts of water at a given time. Having a good source of clean water that is free of hard minerals and chemicals on location at the grow sight is the most ideal situation. Obtaining water from an off-sight source and having it trucked or transported in is an expensive endeavor that consumes both time and money. If the onsight water has undesirable attributes or contaminants, a water filtration system for purification can be installed at a sizeable expense. The days of pumping water from a river or damming a stream are over and doing so can result in quite severe consequences. This is becoming especially true in places like Northern California where prolonged draughts have lead to unprecedented water restriction reforms. Be sure to stay up to date on local water consumption regulations to keep your grow in compliance.

Sunlight:

Equally important to a grow sight is an abundant amount of sunlight. Long days of full sun are the fuel to a successful performance garden. This means full sun to the max. The general rule for annual flowering plants is eight hours of sunlight at the very minimum. Try and choose a south-facing spot that has as little to no shade as possible. If the area has trees that border closely to the sides of the garden, a grower may want to take into consideration a bit of tree removal. The goal is to have a grow sight setup in such a manner that as much sun as possible can reach the majority of the plant for a majority of the time. Trees

Cannabis grown in a performance garden requires full sunlight for a majority of the day. Positioning the garden on a south facing plot of land will ensure that the plants receive the necessary amount of sunlight each day."

not only create unwanted shade that can lead to underperforming plants, but they also create a habitat for a range of creatures like insects/pests, birds, and other small critters that can negatively affect a grow by attacking the plant itself or digging into the soil and damaging the roots. Depending on the amount of plants being grown, one will want to have enough area to space them so that they will not become crowded and shade each other out: a concept that will be explained in further detail at a later point.

Costs & Financing:

The key to a high-performance outdoor cannabis garden is to try and never cut any corners. Just like Hunter S. Thompson once wrote, "If anything's worth doing, it's worth doing right" and in this context that means getting the highest quality supplies and input ingredients that are available. That includes soils, fertilizers and soil conditioners, containers, pumps, and all other materials that will be needed throughout the entire grow and harvest. So to be rather frank, starting and maintaining a high performance garden will be a cost intensive operation. The bulk of the expenses will come at the beginning through acquiring and preparing a garden sight. Note that traditional lenders like banks rely heavily on the Federal Reserve and will usually be unwilling to lend money or set up bank accounts for anything related to cannabis production because the cultivation of cannabis is currently still illegal under federal law. The best ways to finance a performance garden is to either finance it yourself, have reliable private investors/partners, or locate a private lender that is willing to take the risk of the investment.

Climate & Environment:

The growing season for a high performance outdoor cannabis garden can easily extend from late May all the way through mid- to late October. This can vary from location to location, but it is ideal to find an environment with a climate that is not too hot in the deep summer months and not too cold at night in the spring and fall. These types of climates exist in large numbers throughout Northern California and up

Depending on location, growing seasons may vary in length and temperature. Having a strong understanding of the environment chosen will help you make important decisions like when to transplant outdoors and how early or late to harvest.

through the collective northwestern states. Some seasons will be longer than others and selecting strains of cannabis that are suitable for a particular climate is an important step to overall success. When a plant is forced to grow in conditions that are unfavorable, such as extreme heat or cold nights, the growth patterns will be effected which can result in lower performing yields.

By taking these topics into consideration when choosing a sight for a high-performance outdoor cannabis garden, a grower will be starting off on the right path. Staying within the law and having a solid financial backing will provide a firm base for building a successful performance garden.

Chapter Three

Garden Preparation & Set-Up

Once the location for the grow site has been determined and all of the necessary arrangements have been made, then comes the time to begin preparing and setting up the garden. The success of your garden will depend on the sum of its parts. Give every detail, from the minute to the grandiose, careful attention. Properly think through each step along the way. Do not cut corners. Do not half-ass anything. The results of a high performance garden will directly reflect the work that went into it. If you want to achieve notable outcomes that are deserving of praise, you need to put in the hard work, time, and effort that excellent results require. Some of the hardest work in creating a high performance garden will come at this stage of the endeavor. Preparation and set-up of the garden can be a grueling and bruising task but, when done in a thorough, well thought-out manner can result in the perfect canvas on which to create a masterpiece.

Ground Preparation:

Creating an adequate surface for production is the platform of a successful outdoor cannabis garden. The plants should be grown in Smart Pot® fabric aeration containers and can easily reach heights of over 10 feet, so it is imperative to find or create the flattest surface possible. There are several reasons for growing in containers instead of the earthen soil. Some terrestrial soils can hold unwanted containments such as excessive heavy metals or chemical residues from previous misuse and management. Other soils may have an undesired composition like heavy amounts of clay that can lead to poor drainage with a texture that is too dense for delicate roots to effectively traverse through. The best, fool-proof way to avoid these issues is to grow in containers and to know exactly of what the growing medium is comprised.

Given the fact that the plants can grow to extreme heights and will be top-heavy come maturity, it is extremely important that the growing surface be flat. Depending on the current lay of the land this may entail using tools or possibly machinery to create the flattest surface achievable. If the ground has a natural slope, it is recommended to utilize a method of creating flat strips of land along the grade of the slope which is referred to as terracing. If this would entail more work than is feasible a grower can make individual flat spots for each container. The reason why a flat surface is of such high importance is because once these plants reach a massive size any slight angle, along with a strong gust of wind, could result in the whole thing, both plant and container, ending up in a horizontal mess on the garden floor. Having a flat surface will also make any regular maintenance and upkeep chores much easier to complete. While the leveling of the surface is being completed this is also an excellent time to clear out any rocks, grass/weeds, and any other avoidable obstacles from the garden area. Clearing of grass and plants is important because it can be an invitation to bugs and other critters.

When the performance garden has ample amounts of space the maximum container size can be utilized. This garden uses 1,000 gallon containers. Note the gopher wire on the ground beneath the container. The Smart Pot is almost always gopher resistant but a bag full of succulent roots is temptation for pesky rodents. The wire gives extra protection.

Doing so will also help lessen the possibility of them growing into and around the containers. The removal of any rocks and other hard pieces of earth is needed because of the next step of the preparation process.

After creating as flat a surface as possible and removing all rocks and other debris, cover the entire garden area with a heavy-duty landscape fabric or weed mat. The mat should be laid out to cover the whole garden surpassing the containers by at least five to six feet. This will create enough space to allow ease of maneuverability when working in and maintaining the garden. Use the thickest heavy-duty fabric available to ensure that it does not easily rip or tear due to the heavy amount of traffic it may experience. Using cheap, thin fabric will result in rips and tears that allow weeds and grasses to infiltrate the garden. When laying out the weed mat, overlap the edges by 6 to 12 inches and secure in place with ground stakes similar to those used with tents for camping. Overlapping the weed mat will help to create a sort of single-layered structure that is more impervious to weeds, grasses, and small animals.

By mapping out the garden in a grid-like fashion, determine the placement of each individual Smart Pot® fabric aeration container (spacing will be discussed in more detail further along in this chapter). Before the containers are set in place and filled with the growing medium it is an excellent idea to lay down either gopher or chicken wire so it will be located underneath the stationed container. Do so by cutting a square length of wire at a size that will completely contain the circumference of the round container and secure it in place with more ground stakes. The size of the wire square will be directly determined by the size and circumference of the container being used. The wire will act as a barrier to help prevent small burrowing creatures, like gophers and moles that may dig up through the ground and weed mat, from getting into the container and causing unwanted damage to the plant's root system. This can be especially important during seasons of drought when the most abundant source of water may just be that which is being irrigated into the containers when the plants need a drink. The weed mat and wire are important preventative measures when designing a high-performance outdoor cannabis garden and can help assure that no unwanted weeds or critters/pests can enter into the containers causing either competition for water and nutrients or severe destruction of the root zone.

Container Size :

Which container size to grow in can be determined by how much space is available and how many plants are to be grown. For a high-performance outdoor cannabis garden, a grower will want to use the biggest container size that will fit the area for however many plants are intended to inhabit the space. The performance garden method is scalable to the size of any garden, but is designed to maximize plant size and yield; therefore, containers no smaller than 100 gallons are preferred. Two hundred or 300 gallon containers are possibly the most often used. These container sizes work great, but the larger the container; the more plant performance will go up. The difference between a 200 gallon container or a 400 gallon container with regards to inputs and expenses is not all that substantial, but the difference in yields can be. I recommend using Smart Pot® fabric aeration containers for several reasons. Most important of which is their ability to encourage natural root pruning and the development of a substantial root zone. Along the inside edge of the fabric containers is a thin space where oxygen is plentiful, but water is scarce. When the growing end of the root reaches this point the tip of it dies back. This encourages more lateral root growth to take place at the die back point, creating many more root tips than in a normal plastic container. Plants take almost all of their water and nutrients in through the actively growing fibrous feeder root tips. More root tips mean a greater ability to uptake substantially more water and nutrients than a plant with fewer growing root tips. This leads directly to an increase in robust top growth. More top grow means more flower sights and more flower sights mean bigger yields. Plastic containers do not offer this thin gap for oxygen to reside so when the growing root tips hit the edge of the container they don t die back, but instead are simply diverted and continue growing, leading to a spiral effect that will lead to the plant becoming root bound and unable to take in as much water and nutrients as in a Smart Pot® fabric aeration container.

Choose the largest container that will fit comfortably within the space allotted while still providing enough space to work around the plants. These 600 gallon containers are big enough to grow a tremendous plant but still small enough to leave plenty of space for easy maneuvering.

The maximum size container for a high-performance outdoor cannabis garden is 1,000 gallon for plants started by seed and 600 gallon for rooted cuttings or clones. The important thing to remember when choosing the container size is that enough space needs to be provided between each plant to allow for easy access and maneuverability while performing regular maintenance and other garden tasks.

Spacing & Floor Plan:

When determining the spatial aspects of the garden floor plan, be sure to leave enough space in between each container to allow for easy movement throughout the area. This aspect should not be taken lightly as there will be lots of garden maintenance to be done and being able to maneuver easily around and between the plants will make everything go much smoother. The space allotted between each container will also need to reflect the size of the plant when it is in the mature, flowering stages of development. It is also important to space the containers far enough away from each other so that they do not shade each other from the sun during the major portion of the daylight hours. The location of the garden and the layout of the containers must be done in a manner that allows sunlight to reach every part of the plant canopy in as long of duration as possible. If sufficient light does not reach a portion of the plant, the canopy will start to form into a hedge-like structure as the plant develops and leans towards the point of optimal sunlight. The portion that is not receiving proper sunlight will end up being underdeveloped and may not even produce flowers. If even a small amount of

When a performance garden is located on sloping land, the ground should be leveled out utilizing the terracing method. This step may require heavy land moving machinery. The planting area should be flat.

After the ground is level, heavy duty weed matt should be laid out to act as the base of the garden.

the plant does not receive adequate sunlight photosynthesis rates will be lower and overall yields will be reduced.

Leave plenty of space from container to container. It is important to have easy, clear access to each plant, and it is important to keep and maintain that unfettered access throughout the growing cycle. Remember, you will be bringing equipment, including a step ladder, to each plant. Give yourself plenty of room to work and maneuver. When using Smart Pots sized 100 gallon to 400 gallon, space your containers 10 feet apart. This means the space from container side to container side is 10 feet. Remember as the plant grows, the plant will overhang the Smart Pot by 2 or 3 feet. Therefore, if each plant has a three-foot overhang, your 10 foot walkway between containers will become a four-foot path, barely enough room to do your good work. When using Smart Pots sized 500 gallon up to 1,000 gallon, space the containers 12 to 15 feet apart. This will leave a walking space of perhaps six-to-eight feet between plants once your garden matures. On a really large cannabis plant, you will want that much room to work. Do not space your containers more than 15 feet apart. Fifteen feet is the maximum distance needed, more than this is too much.

Irrigation:

Water conservation has become a very real environmental concern. Prolonged droughts and unpredictable weather patterns have lead to regulations that restrict the amount of water a home or land owner can access in several regions. A high-performance outdoor cannabis garden will require relatively high amounts of water, especially in the mature flowering stages, and aggressively restrictive water use will lead to smaller plants and yields. Depending on the location of the garden the sources of water can range from extremely plentiful to rather limited, so it is important to make the most of what is available and to manage water distribution in the most thoughtful and efficient way possible. The best way to ensure proper water distribution while avoiding potential waste is to set up a relatively simple drip-line irrigation system. Drip-line irrigation is the best method of water

Irrigation tubing should be tested as soon as it is installed to make sure it is free of cracks or leaks. This step will also moisten the growing medium before transplanting.

delivery for a container garden. The slower dispersal is the most effective use of water when compared to a sprinkler system or other means of irrigation. Arguably, the most important benefit of a drip-line irrigation system is the fact that the water is distributed through the emitters at low levels over a desired amount of time. This allows the rooting media to more readily absorb higher levels of moisture directly, resulting in less run-off from the bottom of the container and a decrease in potential water waste. As the years go by, water is becoming an extremely precious resource. Properly managing your water in the garden and limiting or eliminating any excess runoff is a huge responsibility for the grower.

The irrigation line runs parallel to the rows of containers, splitting off into a separate individual line at each plant.

Regardless of whether the water supply source is a well or an external containment tank, a pump that is strong enough to move the water from the source location to and throughout the garden is required. There are a multitude of pump styles available on the market today and they range from gasoline fueled to electric powered, even some that utilize solar energy. It is up to the grower to choose the pump that best meets the qualifications for each particular situation. If the property has a well on sight it will come equipped with a submerged pump that should be strong enough for any type of ap-

The irrigation line spirals inwards around the base of each plants, allowing for even water distribution.

plication. When drawing water from an external containment tank, the grower will need to do some research to determine the correct pump size for the operation. Taking into account the amount of water to distribute, the distance from the water source to the containers, and whether or not the ground is sloped, will help a grower to determine which pump is most ideal.

The irrigation line will run directly from the pump to the garden. A ¾ inch main line is ideal and will split off into a ½ inch drip line at each container. Run the main line through the garden so that it passes the sides of every container. At the point where the main line reaches the base of the container place a T splitter with the perpendicular side directed towards the container. From that point run the ½ inch drip-line up and into the container with enough hose length to create a spiral from the outer edge of the container to near the base of the plant. To simplify the installation process a grower should purchase pre-set ½ drip irrigation hoses that have the emitters already in place at 9 inch intervals. Simply cut off a section that is long enough to spiral around the inside of the container, connect it to the main line, and place a proper sized cap on the end. If a grower does not buy a pre-built drip line with the emitters installed they will have to place all of the emitters into the hoses themselves which can be an extensive task. A soaker hose can also be used for the drip-line section of the irrigation system, if desired. After the complete drip-line irrigation system is installed, cap the entire system and secure the main line with the help of U shaped ground stakes or something similar.

Selecting a Growing Medium

When selecting a growing medium choose the best medium that the budget will permit and one which will be most suitable for the given situation. The main type to avoid is terrestrial, earthen soils because they are far too dense for contain-

er culture and will have poor drainage as well as aeration. A lighter, fluffier soil-less growing mix is preferred and will help prevent over-compaction of the rooting medium which will lead to decreased root

Soil-less growing mixes can often be delivered in bulk shipments upon request. Just make sure you have a place to put it all when the truck arrives.

growth and lower levels of oxygen in the root zone. If a limited water supply is not an issue, a mix containing more perlite and peat moss is desired. For gardens that are limited in water supply, mixes containing coco-coir or similar materials may be desired as they will retain moisture for longer durations of time. Fully complete and fortified mixes can be purchased or a grower can create their own custom blends containing both inert and nutrient laden ingredients, if desired (a topic which will be discussed in more detail at a point further in the book). Buying soil mixes in bulk is often a more financially sound method, but the grower should be careful and wary when doing so. Depending on the source of the ingredients, bulk mixes can potentially contain unwanted contaminants and even pests. A grower should use due diligence when selecting a bulk mix and perhaps even have a sample tested ahead of time to see if the mix contains any undesired components. Additional ingredients can be added to nearly any mix and a layer of materials, such as river rocks, may be added particularly to the bottom of the container to enhance its stability as well as drainage capacity.

When choosing a growing medium make sure to pick one that has the ideal water retention capabilities for how often you will be able to provide water.

A performance garden is completely scalable to accommodate any sized area. Leave enough space between each container to allow for fully mature growth while still being able to access the plant.

The overall outcome of a high-performance outdoor cannabis garden is dependent on the grower's ability to avoid cutting corners or taking the cheap way out. The garden is meant to result in a positive financial return in the end. Utilizing the best materials and committing to a "no short cuts" method of development is the best investment a grower can make toward a big return come the end of the season. Paying close, unwavering attention to each aspect of the garden is the best way to ensure success. The following is a short rundown of the main materials needed for proper set-up of the high-performance outdoor cannabis garden.

Supplies Needed for Garden Preparation & Setup:

- ☐ Heavy Duty Landscape Fabric / Weed Mat
- ☐ Gopher / Chicken Wire
- ☐ Adequate Sized Smart Pot. Fabric Aeration Containers
- ☐ Soil-Less Growing Mix / Growing Medium
- ☐ Water Pump For Drip-Line Irrigation
- ☐ ¾-Inch Main-Line Drip Irrigation Hose
- ☐ ½-Inch Drip-Line Irrigation Hose with Pre-Set Emitters / Soaker Hose
- ☐ Or Drip-Line Irrigation Emitters

Chapter Four

Propagation

A successful high-performance outdoor cannabis garden that delivers impressive yields from healthy plants begins on the day the first roots sprout. Cannabis plant propagation can be done one of two ways. The first way is by starting brand new plants from seed. The second is through the rooting of cuttings taken from a donor plant called a "mother," a process of asexual plant reproduction which is commonly referred to as "cloning". Both methods are reliable avenues to take when starting and each one has its own benefits. Considerable care and attention is required throughout the early propagation period since even the smallest mistake or miscalculation can cause unwanted stress on the young plants. When plants experience stressful situations at an early stage of development, growth rates will usually be reduced. Small mistakes can lead to several undesirable results such as plants that mature too early in the season, plants that mature too late in the season, or plants that are highly underdeveloped. By creating and maintaining the ideal environment and situation throughout the early propagation and plant development stages, a grower will be able to ensure their crop will be healthy with high yields.

Seed Propagation

Starting cannabis plants from a reliable seed source is the best way to ensure that the young plant, or seedling, will be pure with regard to the intended genetic makeup of the plant. The advantage of seed propagation over cloning is that propagation limits the chance of predisposition to potential problems a clone plant may inherit from the mother plant. When starting straight from seed, a grower can be confident that the plants he or she is growing will have greater genetic diversity and possibly be more productive. The most important aspect of starting plants in this manner is the source of the seeds. Inferior seeds will lead to inferior plants and yields. If, as a grower, you do not breed your own seeds, then you must be sure to purchase them from the most reliable and respected source available. Seeds from the most respected local sources are always recommended. Buying local is important for good reasons. Seeds that were produced in the same region where the grower lives will come from plants that were bred in that same environment. The resulting seeds will give life to plants that are more genetically adapted to cultivation in the same regional area. Seeds from respected local sources also tend to be fresher or newer which will increase the rate of germination (sprouting) when planting time comes. If they are available locally, seeds that were saved from the previous year's crop are definitely preferred. Try to avoid seeds that are over two years old because the older the seeds, the less reliable they will be. Seeds from foreign sources or from overseas tend to be older and germination rates can be inconsistent, so stick with local well-known seed sources and start the garden off on the right foot.

For seeds to sprout properly they need favorable conditions. The factors that account for such conditions are moisture, temperature, and sometimes light. Cannabis seeds are no exception and will sprout best in warmer, more humid conditions. Starting the seeds indoors in March will ensure that the plants are far enough along in development and size to be planted outdoors come May. To give the seeds a little jumpstart and to help decrease the time it takes to sprout (the germination period), soak the seeds for 24-48 hours

Young plants need to be housed in a greenhouse or hoop house structure. This one is simple and cost effective with roll-up sides for when the weather warms up.

in a solution of sea kelp and water. Sea kelp contains, among other things, naturally occurring plant growth hormones that can help trigger germination of the seed. The plant growth hormone that this reaction is mostly attributed to is the growth hormone called "auxins". A normal, untreated cannabis seed could take seven to 10 days to germinate and sprout its first root, called the "radical". Cannabis seeds soaked in a solution of about one part sea kelp to 100 parts water will begin to sprout their initial radical root in around one or two days. Both concentrated liquid and water soluble powdered sea kelp extracts will work effectively to increase germination rates and times.

Once the seed coat, or shell, has split open and the first root is beginning to emerge, the seed should be sown into a peat seed-starting pellet. Other starting mediums, such as rockwool and potting mix, will work for this step but peat pellets are preferred. They have the ability to hold relatively high amounts of both water and oxygen when they expand, while still maintaining excellent drainage, preventing them from becoming waterlogged. Soak the peat starter-pellets in a warm solution of sea kelp and water that is pH adjusted to around 6.0, a pH level that most plants respond to favorably. Many of the products available for lowering the pH of a solution contain either sulfuric or phosphoric acid. These acids are quite corrosive and can be potentially more dangerous for a grower to handle. If a grower is looking for a less corrosive alternative, a 99 percent citric acid water soluble granular product is an excellent alternative. It is available in multiple sizes and can even be purchased in bulk 50-pound bags. It can also be used to make citric acid stock solutions of various concentrations or mixed into water and nutrient solutions at very small amounts to help lower pH.

Let the peat-starter pellets soak just long enough to completely absorb the solution and then place the sprouted seed about a ¼-inch deep into the center of the pellet. Throughout the entire seedling and early development stage the plants should be watered when needed with the same type of pH-adjusted sea kelp and water solution as described above for the peat starter pellets. Make sure to use warm water and apply the solution to the plants immediately after mixing. The roots prefer warm water

Peat moss starter plugs are a great option that offers excellent water and oxygen holding capabilities. Seeds should be started in horticultural treys with drain holes.

and will grow much more rapidly than when given cold water.

Cannabis seeds need constant warmth to germinate, but they do not require light. However, once the plants begin to produce their first sets of "true leaves" they will require an adequate light source to perform photosynthesis. Photosynthesis is the exchanging of gases, oxygen for carbon dioxide, from the surrounding atmosphere and is an important process in plant growth. The peat starter-pellets with the sprouted seeds planted in them should be placed in a standard 10" x 20" starter tray, with drainage holes. This is a good way to make sure your plants don't stay too wet after a watering and will not sit in water that may become stagnant and low in dissolved oxygen. Roots require high levels of dissolved oxygen from fresh water and sitting too long in water or in a solution can cause the roots to die. The peat starter-pellets will provide some air pruning of the roots on their own. This natural air pruning will lead to more abundant new roots. Next, place a short, two- to three-inch tall humidity dome on top of the tray to help retain moisture and heat within. Mount a four-bulb t5 or t8 fluorescent grow-light fixture with 65K-rated bulbs just above the top of the humidity dome. Keep the lights on for 18 hours each day. Make sure the fixture height is easily adjustable and can be raised when the plants need water or as they grow taller. The fluorescent lights should provide enough heat to encourage rapid growth. Ideal temperatures will be 70-80 degrees Fahrenheit within the dome with a relative humidity between 60-70 percent when sprouting the seeds. If temperatures are too low, then an electric heat mat can be placed underneath the tray.

During the next few weeks, after the tiny plants have completely emerged from the seeds, the seedlings will begin developing several sets of "true leaves". The first sets of leaves that appear are called the cotyledons and will look different than the normal leaves. The sets of leaves that come after those and look like normal leaves are referred to as the "true leaves". During the first weeks that the true leaves are developing, the humidity dome should be removed for a few hours a day. Add more hours each day until the plants are acclimated to the environment and the dome can be permanently removed. Seeds love high humidity, but seedlings do not

Plants should be brought outdoors only after night time temperatures stay above 60 degrees. A staging area will help acclimate the young plants until they are ready to be transplanted. Notice the fencing to help protect the plants from unwanted animal visitors

because it interrupts the two important life-sustaining processes of transpiration and respiration. After the plants, roots, and top growth begin to get crowded it is time to transplant them into a larger container. They should then be moved to the greenhouse, or greenhouse style structure. Make sure the temperature will remain above 60 degrees Fahrenheit at night.

Clones

Starting from rooted cuttings or clones, is the most definite way to ensure that the starter plants will be female in sex and true to the intended strain. In general, clones won't grow as large as plants started from seed, but they can be high-yielding crops when grown properly. Clones cut from a young, fresh donor plant, or "mother" plant, are best. Mother plants to be used as a source of clones for next season should be started from seed in mid-autumn when things in the outdoor garden are winding down. Fresh mothers are recommended because as the plants age the genetics of the clones can begin to degrade and they may even become hermaphrodite or male. Allow the mother plants to become bushy and in early March harvest the clones from the lateral shoots that develop between the stems and the lower branches by cutting them at a 45-degree angle at their base. Clones should be taken from female plants. If a grower does not have the availability to maintain mother plants, then clones should be obtained from locally respected sources. Make sure to verify quality genetics. Also, be sure your clones are free of bugs, pests, and mold before introducing them into your garden.

Immediately after cutting the clone from its mother plant, dip the cut end into a powdered (or liquid) nitrogen-fixing bacteria supplement (Azospirillum brasilense) and place it in high-quality rockwool starter cubes that have been soaked in warm water adjusted to a pH of 6.0. Use 99-percent citric acid to lower the pH of the water just like it is stated in the seed propagation section. Some growers use cloning gels containing synthetic rooting hormones, but that is not really needed when rooting cannabis clones. Rooting hormones are more important when the grower is rooting cuttings of plants, like roses, which have a harder external tissue that does not easily develop roots. As long as the rockwool stays warm and kept moist with pH adjusted water (pH 6.0) the roots will usually pop out on their own. The nitrogen-fixing bacteria just gives them a little boost. House the rockwool-clad clones in a standard 10" x 20" starting tray indoors under a four-bulb t5 or t8 fluorescent growlight fixture with 65 K-rated bulbs just like it was explained for seed propagation. Place a six-inch humidity dome-lid on top to trap the humidity, and set the light fixture just above the dome making sure it is height adjustable so the humidity dome can be easily removed for watering.

Keep the rockwool cubes continuously moist with the pH-adjusted warm water and remove excess water that accumulates in the bottom of the tray. The temperature inside the dome should stay between 70-80 degrees Fahrenheit and the lights by themselves should produce enough heat to maintain this temperature. If it does not, then the addition of a heat pad underneath the tray can be used. At times the clones may appear droopy, but don't worry because this is natural before they develop their roots. In about one to two weeks, roots should begin to emerge from the rockwool. At that time the dome should be removed daily for one- to two-hours to help the clones acclimate to life outside the dome. Remove the dome for longer intervals as more roots begin to form, eventually removing the dome completely. Once the clones are fully rooted and the top growth is perky again it is time to transplant them into a larger container. Unlike the plants started from seeds, the cloned plants can stay inside under artificial lighting, preferably fluorescents, until they will be brought out to the greenhouse in May.

Transplanting & Housing Starter Plants

Plants grown utilizing the high-performance method will be transplanted twice in their lifetime. The first time is when they are small seedlings or rooted clones, and then again when they are placed into their final homes outdoors once the conditions are appropriate. Transplanting will be done the same way for both seedlings and rooted clones. The key to a high-performance outdoor cannabis garden is in the rapid development of an extensive root system. An expansive root system leads to an increased ability to absorb larger amounts of water and nutrients. The more nutrients a plant can access the bigger it can grow. For that reason every container used should be a Smart Pot® fabric aeration container. The initial

transplant from the seedling/clone stage should be into a five- to 15-gallon sized Smart Pot®. A five-gallon container is the absolute smallest a grower should use. Fill the containers with a soil-less potting mix that has a low-to-moderate nutrient charge, but is similar to what will be used in the final outdoor containers. A mix that is mostly comprised of inert materials, such as peat moss, perlite, or vermic-

This plant was started in a Smart Pot Transplanter with down folding sides, which stops root circling. Completely remove the fabric Transplanter, which can be re-used.

ulite, will have a lower nutrient charge when compared to mixes that contain organic materials like earthworm castings, kelp meal, or composts to name a few. The soil-less potting mix can be pre-moistened if desired to create a uniform distribution of water. When transplanting, it is important to not overwater as doing so will slow down the initial root growth, lengthening the amount of time it takes for the plant to recover from the transplant stress and to assimilate to the new container. High-performance outdoor cannabis gardens thrive when growth and development is not interrupted, even for a short time.

To help reduce the stress of being transplanted to a new container the seedlings or clones should be treated with beneficial microorganisms or microbes. The two main microbes that will help the plant recover quickly are the nitrogen-fixing bacteria Azospirillum brasilense and the Arbuscular Mycorrhizae fungi Glomus intaradices. Azospirillum breasilense is a beneficial bacteria that attaches to a growing root, forming small nodules, and that helps convert nitrogen from the atmosphere into plant available forms. Mycorrizae fungi, on the other hand, have the ability to locate and obtain nutrients in the soil mix that may be less available to the roots. The nutrients can become unavailable to the roots for many reasons. They may be in a portion of the growing media that the roots have not or cannot access for some reason, or they might have become attached or bonded at the ionic

When transplanting, create a hole in the growing medium that is big enough to accept the plants entire root mass. Gently place it into the hole and backfill the medium, completely covering the existing roots.

level to an opposite charged soil particle, which is often the case for positively charged phosphorus ions. Mycorrhizae fungi will grow on, as well as within, a plant's roots. It is from that point where they will venture into the rooting medium and create a vast net-like structure of tiny strands of fungi called "hyphae". This net-like structure dramatically increases the overall size and mass of the root system and helps the plant obtain more nutrients. The plant and fungi exist together in a mutually beneficial relationship. The plant receives elemental nutrients that it may not have been able to absorb on its own. The Mycorrhizae fungi receive food in the form of sugars from the roots. Mycorrhizae fungi are plant species sensitive and not all species of the fungi will form this beneficial relationship with all types of plants. The Mycorrhizae species Glomus intaradices is most beneficial to cannabis plants, and inoculants containing this single species alone are recommended.

Most beneficial microorganism supplements are water soluble and some come mixed with a colloidal-type ingredient, such as clay, that helps them stick to the roots. Both inoculants can be either applied directly to the roots or mixed with water and applied. When mixed with water the roots can be soaked briefly in the solution or watered in with it after they are transplanted. To transplant, fill the container nearly to the top and make a hole big enough for the roots to fit comfortably. When placing the seedling or clone into the hole be careful not to disturb and injure the roots. After the plant is placed in the hole spread the potting mix around the base of the plant and add, if needed, enough extra potting mix to cover the base of the plant by two or three inches. Water lightly with the microorganism solution and then place the container underneath the lights.

The environment within the greenhouse structure will need to be properly maintained and controlled for maximum growth potential. Temperature might be the most important aspect, specifically during night time and early morning hours. Never let the temperature drop below 60 degrees Fahrenheit because it will lead directly to slower root growth. Day time temps should not be allowed to reach 90 degrees Fahrenheit with a temperature of 75-80 degrees Fahrenheit being optimum. Since the plants will be placed into the greenhouse structure in early April, day time temperatures will likely not be an issue unless it is an unseasonably warm, early spring. If temperatures begin to rise, provide adequate ventilation and air flow or even consider utilizing a shade cloth on top of the structure. In April, night time temperatures will likely dip into the cold range so supplemental heating may be required. For larger greenhouses, a propane or natural gas heater, depending on location and availability, will be sufficient, and for smaller structures electric heaters are an option. Supplement lighting with t5 or t8 fluorescent lights, using as many as needed to ensure even distribution over all of the plants. Keep the lights about one foot above the top of the plants and adjust them as they grow. The reason for using fluorescent lighting is because they emit light that is primarily in the blue section of the light spectrum. This part of the spectrum is used in the vegetative stage of plant growth and is highly available to the plant during photosynthesis. To maximize plant growth during this stage the plants will need a minimum of 14 hours of light per day. For example, provide the plants with light from 5 AM to 9 PM. While the sun can provide ample light during the peak hours of the day, supplemental lighting will be needed in the early morning and evening. Utilize a timer and program the lights to turn on at 5 AM and then off again around 9 AM when the sun is rising higher in the sky. Likewise, program the lights so they come back on around 5 PM when the sun is beginning to set and then off again at 9 PM. Automating this process will make it much easier for the grower and will ensure the plants receive 14 hours of light each day.

Water the plants when the top one-to-two inches of soil mix is noticeably dry. By sticking a finger into the soil a grower can better judge if it is time to water. Insert a finger, index finger works best, into the soil until it meets the first knuckle. If the soil mix feels moist and chunks of it stick to the finger when pulling it out, then it is not time to water. If the soil mix feels dry and no chunks stick to the finger, then it is time to water. Use just enough water to moisten the whole container while trying to avoid any run-off from the bottom. Make sure the soil mix is allowed to dry out a bit between watering. If the mix remains saturated the entire time, root growth will slow down and in the worst case scenario this can lead to root death and plant failure. The entire time that the plants are in the greenhouse environment they should be fertilized on a weekly basis with liquid nutrients of the growers choosing that are formulated for the vegetative stage of growth. Nutrients that are designed for this stage of the growth cycle will have a higher level of nitrogen (N) and are usually labeled as "grow" or

Water thoroughly and immediately after transplanting. Apply beneficial microorganisms to help alleviate any stress that the plant may have experienced.

"veg" formula. In addition, weekly applications of compost tea will help sustain healthy levels of microorganisms and provide other beneficial substances that will aid the overall resilience of the plant. Further in-depth discussion about fertilization will take place in the next chapter.

Seasonal Timing

When it comes to a high-performance outdoor cannabis garden, seasonal timing is everything. The plants being grown have the potential to become towering giants, but it takes time and should not be rushed. Like the old saying goes: it's not a sprint, it's a marathon. This method is the exact opposite of how cannabis is grown indoors. Indoor plants are grown faster, three months on average, and the result is a smaller plant that will usually yield somewhere between one-to-two pounds per plant. High-performance outdoor cannabis gardens take eight-to-nine months and can yield upwards of eight- to 12-pounds per plant. Do not transplant them into the final outdoor containers until the threat of cold nights and frost has passed. This will likely be in mid-May, but each year can be different. Frost and cold soils will have a serious negative effect on root/plant growth that the plant will have difficulty recovering from. Plants that are brought out too early may also have the tendency to flower earlier than desired and the plant will not reach its maximum potential. If a plant is brought out too late, say mid- to late-June, the plant will not have time grow as large as it possibly could before flowering sets in. Cannabis plants are photoperiod sensitive. This means that their flowering/reproductive cycle is induced by changes in daylight hours. The plants will continue in the vegetative stage of growth through June as the days become longer. At the end of June the summer solstice is reached and the days begin to get shorter. Daylight hours are reduced each day throughout July and August which triggers a switch from vegetative growth to flower development. Working along with seasonal changes is an important component of a successful high-performance outdoor cannabis garden.

Chapter Five

Watering & Fertilizer Regiments

Plants rely on water and elemental nutrients to progress through their different developmental stages. From seed to harvest, adequate amounts of both will be required for maximum growth. Cannabis plants grown outdoors utilizing the high performance method are no exception to this rule. They require frequent applications of both water and fertilizer throughout the season.

Water resides within every individual cell of a plant and is a critical ingredient of photosynthesis. During photosynthesis water combines with carbon dioxide and, with a little help from the energy of light, is converted into carbohydrates and oxygen. Carbohydrates serve as the food energy source for a plants life sustaining metabolic processes. The oxygen is released into the atmosphere through transpiration causing upward pressure within the plant's vascular system allowing for more water to enter the roots. Water also serves as a carrier for elemental nutrients in the soil. The nutrients dissolve in the water, come into contact with the roots, and enter into the plant's vascular system.

There are 16 essential elemental nutrients required to grow a crop. Three of which -- carbon (C), hydrogen (H), oxygen (O) -- come from the air and water, and another 13 that are commonly taken up from the soil. These elements are usually grouped as primary nutrients, secondary nutrients, or micronutrients. The primary nutrients -- nitrogen (N), phosphorus (P), potassium (K) -- are needed by the plant in larger quantities relative to the other nutrient groupings. The secondary nutrients are calcium (Ca), magnesium (Mg), and sulfur (S). Micronutrients make up the largest grouping of plant nutrients but are needed in the smallest amounts. This group is comprised of boron (B), chlorine (Cl), copper (Cu), iron (Fe), manganese (Mn), molybdenum (Mo), and zinc (Zn). A proper fertilizer regiment or program will contain a blend of all these elements at appropriate levels for the plants stage of development. Fertilizer companies offer products that are specially formulated for specific points of growth. For instance, fertilizers that are designed for rigorous stem and leaf growth during the vegetative stage of development will be higher in nitrogen (N) and are often given the moniker grow or veg. Products designed to enhance or increase flower production during the reproductive stage of growth are often named bloom or flower. Fertilizer sources range from completely organic to completely synthetic (inorganic) and there are several brands from which to choose. Before making a fertilizer choice it is important to do research, ask fellow growers, or to consult your local hydroponic store on which fertilizer option would best suit your operation and goals. Providing a balanced fertilizer program throughout the season is an essential component to a successful high-performance outdoor cannabis garden.

Watering

To achieve maximum growth and yield potential, cannabis plants will need frequent and adequate watering. It is important that the plants don t go without water for extended periods of time. Doing so can cause the plants to go into water conservation mode where they close their stomata, stopping respiration/transpiration, and halt the intake of water. This, in turn, reduces the amount of nutrients entering the plant causing an interruption in growth. It is equally important to not allow the soil to stay saturated and overly moist for extended periods of time. This will result in a root zone (rhizosphere) that has compromised levels of dissolved oxygen due to the water becoming stagnant, leading to the potential death of roots and beneficial microorganisms alike. The key is to find that happy medium. Provide enough water each time to ensure the entire container is moist. Then let the top part of the soil dry out enough to encourage the roots to grow in search of the moisture below. As the area where the majority of root growth is found dries out the roots will venture into the areas that still contain moisture. If all of the moisture is allowed to dissipate from the soil the roots will stop growing and possibly die back.

As the plants grow and develop throughout the season, the frequency of watering will accelerate. The amount of time between watering will be longest early in the season. During the first month or two outdoors, a plant's root system and canopy growth will be smaller compared to later in the season. In these early vegetative stages the plants will consume less water and watering can usually take place once every five days. As the plants grow larger more frequent watering will be required. Later in the season this may entail watering every other day.

There are a few ways to assess whether or not the plants are in need of water. The first is by just looking carefully at the plants. If the leaves and branches begin to droop then the odds are the plants have gone into water conservation mode and it is definitely time to water. Check the soil first because plants that are constantly overwatered will also look droopy even though the soil will still be wet. In this case many of the roots have rotted away and the plant cannot take up water. If this happens, the container needs to be allowed to thoroughly dry out in hopes of saving the plant. With that said, waiting for the plant to become droopy because it desperately needs water is in no way the preferred method of judging how often to water. Allowing the soil to get that dry limits the amount of water and nutrients entering the plant and has a negative effect on growth rates. This should only oc- cur if water is being rationed due to availability or cost. Another way to determine when to water is by gently sticking a finger into the top of the soil mix. Carefully, so not to disturb any roots, stick your longest finger into the soil as far down as the second knuckle. If the area is completely dried out then the plant may be ready for a watering. The Smart Pots. themselves can also help you determine if the plants need water simply by touching them. If the sidewalls of the containers feel wet midway down from the top, the plants likely don't need water. This is one of the beneficial features that only fabric aeration containers can provide.

There are several aspects to take into account when estimating the frequency of watering. Of course the amount of rainfall will have a direct correlation to how often the plants will need water, but there are other components as well. The com- position of the soil mix should be taken into consideration. Mediums that have been amended with materials like compost, earthworm castings (vermicompost), or coco coir will have better water retention characteristics and will have lower water requirements. On the other hand, mediums containing plentiful amounts of inert materials like expanded clay pebbles, perlite, rice hulls, or river rock will be quicker to drain and dry out. The faster the moisture can escape the container the more often it will need to be watered. When watering, whether through drip-line irrigation or by hand via a hose, saturate the soil slowly to allow for even distri- bution. Allow about 10- to 20-percent of the amount of water applied to flush through and drain out of the bottom of the container. Doing so will ensure that the entire container is properly moistened. It will also help flush out any unwanted excess fertilizer that may be unavailable to the plant at the moment, reducing the possibility of nutrient lock-out .

Fertilizer Regiments

Organic Fertilizers

Organic fertilizers are usually derived from living plant or animal material. These products are often the by-product of other agricultural industries. For instance, bone and blood meal of porcine (pork) origin are obtained from the slaughtering and processing of pigs intended for the food market. Similarly poultry manure is often collected from egg laying chickens and those that are destined to end up on someones dinner plate. In both of these cases, as well as others alike, the obtained by-product materials are further processed, usually with high heat and steam to eliminate any possible pathogens. By the time the products are packaged they are considered safe for plants, pets, and humans alike. Organic fertilizers that are of plant origin like alfalfa meal and kelp meal (though technically not a plant but an algae) are more often than not harvested in a sustainable way with minimal impact on the environment. For products like alfalfa meal, the alfalfa needed for human or animal use is removed and then the rest of the plant is processed into an organic fertilizer product. The key idea behind organic fertilization is an emphasis on sustainability and limiting waste by using as many parts of the animal or plant as possible.

These days, true organic fertilizer products must receive certification from one of a number of organizations dedicated to upholding the integrity of the market. The most popular organic certification at the moment is the listing of a product on the OMRI (Organic Materials Review Institute) database. If a material is listed as OMRI certified then the grower can have some piece of mind knowing that the product is produced in accordance to approved methods. There are also state and federal agencies that certify products as organic. On a federal level products can obtain the NOP (National Organics Program) certification which is overseen by the USDA. Currently, the most popular state certifications come from the CDFA (California Dept. of Food & Agriculture) and the WSDA (Washington State Dept. of Agriculture) organic material input programs. Products

Granular products can be mixed in with the growing medium to provide proper nutrition throughout the vegetative stage.

that are labeled with one or all of these certifications have been thoroughly vetted and are found to be in compliance with national organic standards.

There is a wide variety of organic material that can be used for plant fertilization. Some popular ingredients include bone meal, blood meal, seabird/bat guano, ground oyster shells, composted poultry manure, feather meal, alfalfa meal, kelp meal, and earthworm castings. A grower can purchase separate ingredients and blend them together to create mixes for each specific growth stage. This is the more difficult way of approaching organic fertilization and will require a decent understanding of the materials and the plant's nutritional needs. If you wish to blend your own mixes it is advised to use a light respirator or dust mask when doing so. Or you can go the easier route and trust the professionals with your organic nutrient needs. There are several companies that offer pre-mixed granular organic fertilizers utilizing many of the same ingredients listed above. Purchasing pre-mixed blends will be more cost intensive but it will also take the guesswork out of the equation. Pre-mixed products will be specifically formulated or blended to meet the plant's nutrient needs for each of the developmental stages. Most companies offer separate pre-mixed blends designed for vegetative growth and enhanced flower development. There are even high potassium (K) blends to be used as a finishing product that adds bulk to the flowers before harvest. Using pre-mixed blends will cut down on the amounts of individual bags needed and provide the plants with a balanced nutrient regiment.

The mix to be used for the vegetative growth stage can be blended into the soil mix before the plants are transplanted in the spring. Follow the suggested application rates provided by the manufacturer. They should include simple application rates like, use such and such amount per gallon of container size . This will provide a baseline nutrient level that will feed the plant for a good three to four weeks. Blend the fertilizer into the medium in early April when the temperatures are still relatively low. As the weather warms the soil, microbial life will become active and start the process of breaking down the organic matter. Giving the microorganisms a head start will help ensure that the fertilizer will be readily available when it comes time to transplant. After transplanting, the fertilizer should be applied every three to four weeks throughout

An in-line timer helps give the proper applications of both water and fertilizer. This is especially helpful when the garden is left unattended for long periods of time.

the season. Applications can be made using the top dress method. When top dressing with granular organic fertilizer, spread it evenly over the soil mediums surface and gently blend into the top inch or so. Be careful not to damage the plants roots. Most dry organic fertilizers will include application directions for top dressing. After the fertilizer is applied simply water it in lightly and let the beneficial microbes do their work. The mix designated for the vegetative growth stages will be used until mid-August, when the plants will begin to flower. At this point, you will want to switch to the mix that is formulated for flower development. If you are going to use a finishing mix do so during the last three to four weeks before harvest. Liquid organic fertilizers such as kelp, humic/fulvic acid, molasses, and fish protein hydrolysate can be used supplementary during the entire season. These can be applied directly to the soil or sprayed on the plants foliage and will provide extra food for beneficial microbes as well as readily available nutrients for the plants. However, depending on the location, liquid organic fertilizers may not be the best option for your garden unless there is a cool place to store them. When left outside or in a shed under the hot summer sun these types of products will become biologically active and the microorganisms found within them will begin decomposing the product. This can result in the containers becoming bloated and possibly exploding from the pressure of the gasses being created inside; the smell of which will certainly be horrendous. Believe me, almost nothing smells worse than liquid fish protein baking in the hot summer sun.

The fact that more often than not organic fertilizer materials come from plant or animal origin means they behave in different ways compared to synthetic (inorganic) fertilizers. By definition, organic matter contains plant nutrients that are held together with a carbon (C) bond, commonly referred to as an organic matrix. This means that the nutrients will not be completely available to a plant's roots until the carbon (C) bond is broken. Breaking this bond takes the help of specialized bacteria and fungi whose jobs in nature are to aid in the decomposition of organic matter, releasing the constituent elements held within in an ionic form. This is the form that plant roots are able to absorb. If a high performance garden is to be successfully grown utilizing organic fertilization methods then the grower will need to ensure that there are plentiful amounts of microbial life in the rhizosphere. There will naturally be a base line population of microbial life already present in the soil if conditions are favorable. But there are steps that can be taken to increase the levels of these beneficial microorganisms. Inoculating the roots and soil medium with supplemental microbial life at transplant time as well as throughout the season can raise their overall levels. Perhaps the best way to encourage robust microbial life throughout the season is by weekly applications of a compost tea. Compost teas can be made from numerous organic materials, the most popular being earthworm castings. The materials are steeped in filtration bags, like big tea bags, and brewed in highly oxygenated water for 24-48 hours with the help of an external air pump. The high levels of dissolved oxygen encourage rapid microbial growth which will add to the populations in the medium when it is applied. Having high levels of active beneficial microorganisms will result in an accelerated breakdown of organic material into plant available nutrients. It will also make the plants and their roots more resistant to soil-borne pathogens and disease.

Synthetic (Inorganic) Fertilizers

The main benefit of using synthetic fertilizers is the fact that the nutrients are already in their ionic form and are immediately available for uptake by the roots. Unlike organic fertilizers, synthetic nutrients do not require decomposition and conversion by soil microorganisms. Synthetic fertilizers are most often manufactured from mineral salts that are mined from the earth and processed into water soluble forms. This makes them a less sustainable choice when compared to organics. However, their ease of use and quick acting reliability makes them a popular fertilizer choice for cannabis gardens indoors and out. There are countless numbers of synthetic nutrient providers to choose from and most offer the same types of products. Synthetic nutrient lines will usually consist of two separate base nutrient products that contain the majority of the nutrients. These products will be split up into one formulated for vegetative growth and one for flower development. Along with the base nutrients most companies will offer a calcium (Ca) and magnesium (Mg) additive referred to as CalMag that is an important part of the nutrient line. The majority of synthetic base fertilizers do not contain calcium (C) and magnesium (Mg). This is because these two elements do not mix well together with the other nutrients in a concentrated solution. Instead they will need to be added, with the base, to an adequate amount of water so that they can stay in solution. Most synthetic fertilizer lines will have multiple supplement products but all are not essential when growing an outdoor cannabis crop. There are also emerging nutrient companies that are creating all-in-one base nutrients, eliminating the need for numerous inputs. You should do extensive research before purchasing to decide which supplement will most benefit the operation.

Water soluble or liquid fertilizer concentrates deliver vital nutrients to the growing plant.

When deciding which brand of synthetic fertilizer to use it pays to keep in mind that companies with inferior nutrient lines do not last long. If a product or line of products does not perform well growers will stop using it and word will spread. Companies and products that have passed the test of time can be trusted to provide consistent, positive results. Consulting with respected growers, combing through the many Internet forums, and chatting with employees or owners of hydroponic shops are all excellent ways to get a finger on the pulse of what is working for others. If a line of products is being touted by numerous groups of growers then the odds are it will work for you. This may require going top shelf with regard to price but one must remember that in order to have a successful high performance outdoor cannabis garden no meaningful expense should be spared. Fertilizer is an immensely important part of a productive garden and the best possible products should be used. Since there are so many different products in any given line it makes sense, and is easiest to stick with, using products from a single company s line. Try to avoid using separate individual products from several different companies. This is not so much about being worried about the quality of other brands, but more an issue of compatibility. Products formulated for a single fertilizer line will be designed to mix and interact favorably with other products in the line. Also, if there is an issue with compatibility the company will provide in the directions special mixing instructions to avoid complications. Bringing in a product from another company s line may cause unwanted interactions between the elements or drastic pH fluctuations that can cause certain nutrients to fall out of solution.

Using synthetic fertilizers does come with inherent complications. Synthetic fertilizers will need to be mixed with water before they can be applied. This means that some sort of tank or container will be required for mixing up a batch. The size of the mixing apparatus should somewhat reflect the number of plants in the garden and the size of the containers but, generally speaking, the bigger the tank the better. Bigger tanks mean fewer fertilizer batches are needed to be mixed for each feeding. A 250-gallon plastic IBC tote is a great choice for mixing larger amounts of fertilizer. They have a large hole in the top where the water and fertilizer can be added and an electric mixing blade can be easily mounted. IBC totes also have a handy discharge valve at the bottom and attachments can be purchased for the addition of a pump to pull the fertilizer solution from the tote to be delivered to the plants. There are even attachments that will circulate the water from the bottom discharge back up to the hole on the top. This is a great way to mix a large batch of fertilizer without a mixing blade and motor.

Some fertilizer companies will offer feeding schedules that make the fertilization process less daunting. The schedules are complete fertilization programs broken down into weekly application regiments. These are an excellent reference tool and help take the guesswork out of fertilizing the garden. Lower rates of the concentrated fertilizer can be used for growing outdoors than compared to indoors, so start at half the rate suggested unless the company has a specific feeding schedule designed for outdoors. An EC/ppm meter is helpful when using synthetics. These meters will measure the amount of dissolved mineral salts in the solution by determining its electric conductivity (EC)-- how well it conducts electricity. A solution with more dissolved mineral salts will have a higher EC. With this number a simple equation will help you determine the amount of fertilizer in the solution in parts per million (ppm), EC x 500 = ppm. A safe ppm to start off with early in the season would be around 300-500 total or 0.6-1.0 EC., and try to avoid a ppm of over 1,000 (EC 2.0) at anytime in the season. Adjust the pH of the solution to around 6.0 before applying.

A high performance outdoor garden will need to be fertilized one to two times a week when using synthetics, with regular watering between feedings. Using lower feeding rates will help ensure that you dont over fertilize. If you have the ability, the fertilizer can be distributed through the dripline irrigation system. Just make sure to run some water through the lines after each feeding to avoid any fertilizer salt build-up in the emitters. Feeding can also be done with a hose and a sprayer or watering wand. This will require an electric (or gas) water pump that is strong enough to move the solution to the containers. Regardless of the method used

the solution should be applied to the soil until it begins to flow out the bottom of the container. Only foliar feed as needed to fix minor nutrient deficiencies or to apply some type of specialty product. When watering between feedings allow 10 to 20 percent of the water to exit the bottom of the container. This will reduce the amount of residual fertilizer salts that can build up in the soil by flushing them out. Without regular flushing these mineral salts can accumulate and cause fertilizer

A hand held watering wand is an excellent tool for applying both water and fertilizer to the plants. For smaller gardens this method can be used instead of an irrigation system.

imbalances in the medium resulting in unwanted but avoidable consequences. Collecting some of the water runoff and testing the EC/ppm levels is an excellent way of determining if the plant is being fed too often or at too high a rate. If the EC/ppm is higher than what the previous feedings was then you may need to cut back on feeding strength or frequencies and flush with normal watering until the number is lower. As is the case with organic fertilizers: feed with the vegetative cycle products until August and then switch to the flowering cycle products. If you wish to use a finishing product do so a few weeks before harvest and allow time for a good week of straight water flushing.

Hybrid Method

The hybrid method of plant nutrition is a tried and true approach utilized by growers in nearly all sectors of horticulture. The hybrid method makes for an excellent fertilization program when it comes to growing cannabis. This approach utilizes both the organic and synthetic forms of plant nutrition giving the grower, and the plant, the best of both worlds. The reason the hybrid method is so effective is that the organic components being added to the soil medium help to build and sustain populations of beneficial microorganisms. The beneficial microorganisms in turn help break down the organic matter, releasing the nutrients held within for consumption by the plant. They also help create a healthy root zone that is less capable of supporting harmful soil pathogens. As the organic fertilizer works below the surface creating a healthy root environment, the applications of synthetic fertilizer provides fast acting, reliable plant nutrition. This is what makes the hybrid method so effective. The grower is developing a sustainable microbial population that increases the health and potential of the soil while at the same time supplying adequate plant nutrients that go to work immediately, resulting in a healthier plant that is more productive. Feed the soil and the plant.

When utilizing the hybrid fertility method apply both organic and synthetic fertilizers at half the suggested rate. Top dress with the organic nutrients once a month and apply a compost tea on a weekly basis. Apply the liquid synthetic fertilizer solution weekly at half, or even a third, of the suggested label rates. Foliar

The hybrid method of fertilization utilizes synthetic blends balanced with organic methods.

applications should only be made as needed or if desired for a certain product. Similar to the other fertilization methods, switch from vegetative to flowering products in August as the plant begins to flower. When done appropriately, the hybrid method will result in an extremely healthy plant that delivers a high quality, exceptional yield.

Supplies Needed For Watering & Fertilization

Watering Supplies

- ☐ Reliable Water Source
- ☐ Irrigation Lines / Water Hose & Sprayer or Wand

Organic Fertilizing Supplies

- ☐ Container For Mixing Ingredients (if you create your own blends)
- ☐ Dust Mask
- ☐ Measuring Scoops

Compost Tea Supplies

- ☐ Large Bucket or Small Tank for Mixing
- ☐ Aeration Pump and Air Stone
- ☐ Compost Tea Ingredients
- ☐ Large Tea Bags or Nylon Stockings

Synthetic Fertilizer Supplies

- ☐ IBC Tote or Tank for Mixing Solution
- ☐ Mixing Blade & Motor or Pump for Recalculating Mix in IBC Tote
- ☐ High Powered Pump for Delivering Solution
- ☐ Irrigation Supplies (ie) Hoses, Watering Sprayer or Wand
- ☐ EC/ppm Meter
- ☐ pH Meter
- ☐ Measuring Cups or Container

Chapter Six

Plant Caging & Support

When growing an outdoor cannabis garden, effective plant support is crucial. All of the comfortable reliability that is inherent to growing indoors goes out the window and is replaced with uncertainty. Mother Nature has a tendency to throw unexpected and often harsh conditions into the mix. Heavy rains, winds, and even hail are all possibilities when growing in the great outdoors. If your plants fall over at any time during the season they may not survive. If they do, the stress put on them has the potential to ruin the crop or substantially decrease yields. All of your hard work and money will be wasted. To combat unexpected weather tendencies the best offense is a good defense. A proper plant support system is like an insurance plan. Take the time and effort to make the supports strong enough to withstand harsh conditions and you will be rewarded with a bountiful harvest.

By following the plant caging, trellising, and support guidelines detailed in this chapter you can be rest assured that each plant will be equipped with an adequate defense system against the most severe outdoor weather conditions. The plants will be able to grow continuously without major issues and achieve their optimal yields. This book is geared towards maximum production and many of the descriptions are for the largest container size; however, it is important to remember that this method is entirely scalable to any size. The methods described can be adjusted to any container size and will help you grow an outdoor cannabis plant to its full potential.

Internal Caging

A reliable plant support system starts with internal caging. The internal caging will act as the baseline support for the entire plant. Its job is to provide stability to the main stem and the internal branches that will grow out to eventually develop flowers. This is why the internal caging must be as strong and resilient as possible. Heavy-duty tomato cages, such as the Texas tomato cage, have large circular rungs, are extremely durable, and come in taller sizes. Depending on the size of the container the internal caging should be anywhere from four to six feet tall. This will allow for complete stabilization of the entire trunk of the plant. I say trunk instead of stem because in a high performance outdoor cannabis garden the plants can end up being more like trees. This fact is the reason why proper caging and support is so important.

The internal caging can also be constructed manually with only a few materials needed. Simply place four heavy-duty bamboo stakes around the plant in a pattern that creates a square shape when straight lines are drawn from stake to stake. Then wrap a durable wire cage with six-inch-square holes around the outside of the four stakes and secure it with heavy-duty gardeners twine or bailing wire in several places. Vinyl coated wire caging works well since it is flexible, strong, and the coating is much gentler on the stems/branches compared to non-coated. Metal concrete rebar grids also work well for the internal caging. They are extremely strong and come pre-set with six-inch square holes. But they can be somewhat difficult to work with. The rebar grid will have to be rolled into a circular shape and the ends will need to be secured properly. If it is an option, welding the ends together is the best way to go, but twisting a thick gage wire around the connecting ends will work as well. If you choose either of these methods of internal caging, make sure that the structure is between four to six feet tall to give the plants the best support. The diameter size of the internal caging and its distance from the plant base will vary depending on the size of the container used. For container sizes from 600 to 1,000 gallons the diameter of the cage should be around 24 inches. With the plant in the center of the caging this

A heavy duty tomato cage serves as the internal caging for this plant, providing a central point of stability.

will allow for 10 to 12 inches of space from the plant stem to the caging on all sides. When growing in smaller containers ranging from 500 to 200 gallons, the distance from the plant in the center of the container to the caging itself should be somewhere between six to 10 inches on all sides. Allow for no less than six inches of space between the plant stem and the caging for the smaller containers.

Installation of the internal caging should take place immediately after transplanting into the final outdoor container. This ensures that there will be minimal or no damage to the plants root system when the caging is erected. Waiting for even just a few days will allow the roots to start growing in exploration of their new home, and when the cage or stakes are put into the ground the risk of severing them is higher. So, just after transplanting, assemble the internal cage making sure the base or stakes are buried deep enough in the soil to provide a secure anchor. Installing the internal caging to a depth of around six inches should provide enough baseline support to give the plant stability throughout the season.

External Caging

The main purpose of the external caging is to provide support to the outer branches that will eventually develop flower buds, but it will also help stabilize the internal caging as well. A strong external caging will ensure that the branches do not bend or break from their size and the weight of the flower buds. By using the combination of internal and external caging you can be sure that the entire plant is properly supported. The technique described here is relatively easy to assemble and can be scaled down to work with any size container.

First, you will need to pound four, eight- to 10-foot tall heavy-duty metal T-posts into the ground just outside the outer walls of each container. Hammer the T-posts down at least a foot into the ground so that it is securely anchored and cannot easily be removed. Arrange

External caging should be installed long before the plant grows large. This allows the branches to grow directly into the caging.

the T-posts in such a pattern that if a line was drawn to connect all four posts the shape of the line would be square. The end result will be a circular container with a square-shaped cage rising above it. After the T-posts are in their respective places, the internal caging should be secured to the outer posts with heavy-duty gardeners twine of bailing wire. Each side of the internal caging will need to be connected to the outer T-post nearest to it in at least three points. Doing this provides more stability to the internal caging and creates one solid structure that can withstand the harshest of weather conditions. Once the internal caging is secured to the external caging posts, the posts will need to be wrapped vertically in either heavy-duty vinyl coated caging or wire fencing that has six-inch square holes throughout. As stated earlier, vinyl coated wire caging is ideal because of its strength, flexibility, and the fact that the vinyl coating will be gentler on the branches themselves.

The external caging should be started about one to two feet above the top of the container to allow easy access for feeding/watering, inspection of rooting medium, irrigation repairs, and any other maintenance that may need to be done. When completed the external caging should reach the top of the T-posts so there are no gaps in the support system and there are enough six-inch holes to accommodate every outer branch. Regardless of the type of material being used for the external caging--be it vinyl coated wire caging or wire fencing--it will need to be tightly secured with heavy-duty gardeners twine or bailing wire to each T-post in at least four points on each individual post. After everything is properly secured

The external caging should be placed at least one foot above the top of the container, allowing for easy access and maintenance.

the external caging will be complete and ready to support the growing plant.

The external caging does not have to be assembled right away after transplanting the plants outdoors like the internal caging does. Depending on the container size, it will take some time for the plant to grow to the point where the outer branches begin to approach the side walls of the container. However, it is imperative that the external caging be in place before the branches reach the point where the caging will reside. Waiting too long creates a considerable amount of hassle when assembling the external caging as you need to carefully maneuver each branch into its respective six-inch hole. Putting the caging in place before the outer branch growth reaches that point makes things go more smoothly. It also puts less stress on you and the plant.

By the time the plants are ready for the final trellising they will be quite large. Use a ladder.

The final trellising provides stability to the top portions of the plant which take on a considerable amount of weight as the flowers develop.

Final Trellising

The final trellising will be in charge of supporting the top portion of the plant canopy. For this portion of the plant support system you should use either the vinyl-coated wire caging or plastic horticultural netting with six-inch square holes. The final trellising will be layered horizontally and properly secured at each corner to the four outer T-post used for the external caging. The first layer of horizontal trellising should be placed just above the top of the internal caging. Additional layers should be put into place every one to two feet until the tops of the T-posts are reached. The layering of the horizontal trellising will provide much needed support to the top branches and complete the plant support system.

As was the case with the external caging, the individual layers of the final trellising will need to be in place before the growing plant reaches that point. However, assembling the final trellising will be extremely difficult when the external caging is completely in place so the two steps should be completed at about the same time.

Single lengths of caging laid horizontally can be used for the final trellising.

Following the techniques and steps outlined in this chapter will ensure that each plant has a strong, reliable support system. It will also give you some peace of mind in knowing that even during the most intense wind gusts or storms, the plants will be safe and remain upright. Avoiding the complications that come with improperly or under-supported plants is a substantial step in creating a high-performance outdoor cannabis garden that yields impressive results.

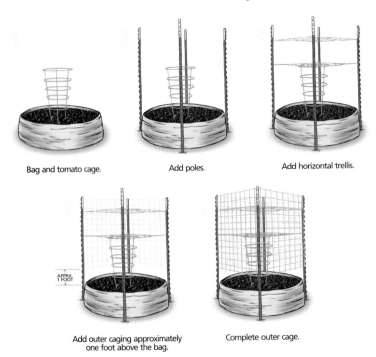

Bag and tomato cage.

Add poles.

Add horizontal trellis.

APPROX.
1 FOOT

Add outer caging approximately one foot above the bag.

Complete outer cage.

Chapter Seven

Pest Control

A truth that is always self-evident when growing cannabis is the importance of a well-rounded pest control program. Agonizing attacks from multiple pests big and small are inherent in outdoor growing. If pests are allowed to run unchecked, your crop will become an inviting place for them to eat, breed, and live out their lives, thereby leading to the devastation of plant loss or lowered yields. Investing in a multi-faceted approach to pest control is like having an insurance plan for your garden. Spending the time and money it takes to keep hostile pests away is a crucial step toward having a successful garden.

When establishing a working pest control program be sure to keep in mind that it needs to be done in a way that utilizes natural and organic products. The end harvest and any subsequent products made from it will be intended, in some form or another, for human consumption. For a high-performance outdoor cannabis garden to maintain any amount of integrity it first and foremost must be free of any chemical pesticides or insecticides that might have possible carcinogenic (cancer causing) properties. This is a medicine that thousands of people rely on and the safety of the end user is of utmost importance. Fortunately, there are an abundance of natural and organic pest/insect control products available on the market today.

Natural and organic pest control products are different from the chemical alternatives in one major way. Because they are less toxic when compared to the chemical alternatives, many pests and insects can build up immunities to natural and organic control products when the same product is used repeatedly. This is not the case with chemical pesticides and insecticides which have the same result with every application, but they are potentially harmful to humans. With this in mind, a proper natural and organic pest control program should be comprised of multiple products that are used in a rotating fashion. Using several products, at least three to four for good measure, which change from application to application, will ensure that the targeted pests do not build up immunities to the individual active ingredients. If the pests are unable to create the immunities, then the products should be effective with every application.

A successful multi-tiered approach to pest management should include some of the following products: biological components such as beneficial microorganisms, natural-based mild contact killers, and plant derived pesticide/insecticide compounds. When these products are used in rotation they will help deter and prevent attacks from the majority of pests. The following are some natural and organic pest control products that work well for outdoor cannabis plant protection and can be used in a simple week by week pest control program.

A healthy crop makes a temping treat for pests. A well rounded pest control program is a must.

Biologicals

An efficient pest control program starts with a strong biological foundation. Regular soil applications, at least once a month, of beneficial bacteria and fungi will help create a healthy, robust root zone (rhizosphere). A root zone that is fortified with beneficial microorganisms will be much more resilient and resistant to attacks from harmful pests and other soil-borne diseases. The initial application of beneficial bacteria and fungi should take place the very first time the plants are transplanted and be followed up with consecutive applications done throughout the entire season. Biologically active compost teas should be incorporated into this aspect of pest control as well. Bi-weekly applications to the soil will help to reinforce the biological fortification of the root zone throughout the season. Replenishing the beneficial microorganisms is an important step because some of the other components in a complete pest control program can be harmful to the soil microbes. Though the other products are applied to the plant's leaves it is still possible that some will run off and end up in the soil medium. Applying supplemental beneficial bacteria and fungi will ensure that the root zone remains properly protected. A healthy root zone will lead to a healthy plant that is strong enough to withstand life outdoors. Similarly, foliar applications of the compost teas should be done at least once a month after the plants are transplanted into their final outdoor container. This will create a healthy leaf surface environment that will be resistant to attacks from pests.

The main way that the biological component of a complete pest control program differs from the rest is that it generally does not kill any pests or insects. Instead it provides a healthy foundation that allows the plant to be less susceptible to external attacks in the first place. With that said, there are some biological products that are more aggressive than oth-

Applying an organic pesticide.

ers. Take for instance the soil bacteria Bacillus thuringiensis (BT). This beneficial bacterium has the ability to act as a biological pesticide and effectively poison the insects that consume it. BT can form protein crystals that contain an efficient insecticide compound. After a pest consumes the crystals, the digestive enzyme protease breaks them down releasing the toxins from within. There are several BT products available on the market today and most come in a liquid form that is safe, when mixed with water, to spray on the entire plant. Other living creatures that can be beneficial to the protection of a cannabis plant through consuming smaller pests are ladybugs and praying mantises. If you decide to purchase either of these, keep in mind that there is no assurance that they will stay to protect the garden and not just go on their merry way. You, as the grower, can also help defend against unwanted pests in the garden by keeping a close eye out and inspecting the plants on a regular basis.

Azadirachtin

Azadirachtin is a botanical insecticide/miticide that is effective on over 200 different types of insects and is of extremely low toxicity to humans and other mammals. The organic azadirachtin compound is extracted from the seeds of the Neem tree (Azadirachta indica) and is readily biodegradable, causing no harm to the plant or its roots. It works by entering the insect by being ingested or absorbed through the body and acts as a feeding inhibitor as well as a growth disruptor. The pests will essentially starve to death while being unable to properly reproduce.

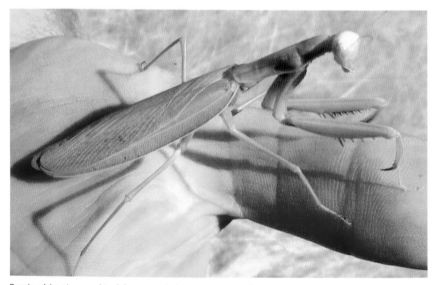

Praying Mantises and Ladybugs can help protect your plants

There are numerous types of azadirachtin products available to growers ranging from oil-based liquids to water soluble powders. Many of these products are certified organic and OMRI listed, making it a safe and reliable addition to any pest control program.

Keeping complete efficacy and reliability in mind, it is often best to use a water soluble powdered form of azadirachtin, especially if you plan on doing several applications throughout the season. Most liquid azadirachtin products are oil based and have relatively low levels of the active ingredient. These products, when used at normal recommended rates, do not provide enough azadirachtin to properly execute the pests. Instead the oils merely coat and suffocate the insects leaving those that survive to develop immunity to the azadirachtin compound which will likely be passed on to their offspring. When this happens the product becomes ineffective and an obsolete component of the pest control program. Using more than the recommended rate of the oil-based liquid products in an effort to raise the concentration levels of the azadirachtin will only result in a solution that has heavy amounts of the natural oil base. Spraying this solution onto the foliage of the plants has the potential to coat or clog the leaf stomata and severely disrupt the highly important transpiration process (how the plant breathes). Higher concentrations can also burn leaf tissue. The best way to avoid this while still maintaining adequate levels of azadirachtin in the spray solution is by using the water soluble powdered version of the product. The water soluble powder does not contain any natural oils. The exclusion of the oils allows it to be mixed with water at higher concentrations. The resulting solution will be more effective at eliminating the targeted pests while avoiding any potential harm to the plant's transpiration process.

Pyrethrins

Pyrethrins are a class of organic compounds that are derived from the Chrysanthemum plant (Chrysanthemum cinerariifolium). These compounds have insecticidal properties and attack the nervous system of the targeted pests, leading to a loss of motor coordination and paralysis. Pyrethrins have been approved by the Environmental Protection Agency (EPA) for more insecticidal uses than any other botanical derived product and they are effective in the elimination of most types of insects. When used properly they present almost no risk to humans and other mammals. Their efficiency and low risk potential make pyrethrins the most commonly used botanical insecticide on the market. There are synthetic versions of pyrethrins, called pyrethroids, which are also used as insecticides but are not organic or readily biodegradable. With the health and safety of you and those who may consume your product in mind, the organic plant-derived pyrethrins should be the only type used.

As was the case with the azadirachtin, it is best to use a pyrethrin product that is of a higher percentage concentration of the active ingredient. Most pyrethrin products available are between one- to two-percent of the active ingredient. Though pyrethrins work reasonably well, the lower level concentrations bring with them the potential of inadequately poisoning the pests. This leaves room for them to possibly develop immunity to the product. Though they are often hard to find at a normal growing supply store, the best organic pyrethrin products to use are those that are above five percent of the active ingredient. When used at normal label rates these higher concentrations will effectively eliminate the pests and still remain safe to use.

Spinosyns/Spinosad

Spinosyns are organic compounds created through the fermentation of the bacteria species Saccharopolyspora spinosa. There are over 20 natural types of spinosyns but the two that are most known for their insecticidal properties are spinosyn A and spinosyn D. These two forms are mixed together after fermentation to create the popular organic insecticide ingredient spinosad. Spinosad is a component of many organically certified and OMRI listed insecticide products and presents little risk of toxicity to humans and other mammals. Spinosyns and spinosad work best through ingestion by the pests but can also have a desired effect simply through contact. The organic compounds in spinosad target the nicotinic acetylcholine receptors causing a severe disruption to the pest's nervous system, leaving most dead within one to two days. Like most natural insecticides or pesticides, spinosad works best on smaller insects and larvae, but is still able to eliminate larger bugs like caterpillars. The best thing about spinosad is that it is not very effective on beneficial insects like predatory mites and will leave most of them alive to do their daily pest control duties.

Mark your calendar! Note your plant maintenance and watering activities.

Contact Killers

Natural and organic contact killers are a key component to rounding out a successful pest control program. As the name implies, contact killers are proficient at eliminating nearly any pest or insect that it comes in contact with. These types of products are known to target pests but they can also be effective at mitigating fungal attacks like powdery mildew. There are even contact killers that are designed for use within the growing medium to counter soil pathogens like pythium or root rot. The fact that contact killers work on nearly every insect/pest that they reach means it will also kill beneficial insects and soil microorganisms, so regular applications of supplemental microorganisms and compost tea are important to revitalize the life around the root zone.

Most natural and organic contact killers contain multiple ingredients that have different modes of action in terms of pest elimination efficacy. The following ingredients are typically found in proficient non-chemical contact killers. Most products will contain a low level of organic oils, such as garlic or soybean oil, which help spread the product over the plant's foliage while at the same time trapping and suffocating the insects or pests. They also tend to contain light acids, such as citric acid, that are harmless to humans and other mammals but have the ability to repel most pests. Alcohol is also found in nearly all natural and organic contact killers. It is included because of its ability to dehydrate the bodies of the pests and insects that it contacts which leads to almost certain death. This is also profoundly useful when battling fungal attacks like powdery mildew as these fungi thrive in high humidity environments. The alcohol dries out the surface of the fungi and prevents it from further growth. The alcohols evaporate relatively quickly and will not leave any trace residues. Natural and organic contact killers can only eliminate the pests or insects that they touch so make sure to apply the product properly over the entire network of stems and foliage for best results.

These are just some of the many different natural and organic pest control products available to consumers. The important thing to remember is that the true purpose of a natural and organic pest con-

Visually inspect your plants for possible insect issues.

trol program for a high-performance outdoor garden is prevention. The best way to deal with potential pest problems is by not allowing them to occur in the first place. When allowed to progress, a pest or disease issue can cause serious damage and can lead to insurmountable damage to the crop. So your best course of action is to never allow any pests the opportunity to occupy the plants for an extended amount of time.

This preventative need is why a proper pest control program needs to be started early and should include a variety of products in rotation to avoid any possibility of the pests becoming immune. Using three or four different natural and organic pesticide/insecticide products in conjunction with applications of a natural contact killer is perhaps the best approach. Start the pest control process at the time of the first transplant from the propagation tray into the five- to 15-gallon Smart Pot® fabric aeration containers. The first application should be just the natural contact killer. This will lower the possibility of bringing any unwanted pests into the greenhouse type structure that will house them until the final transplant outdoors. Plants can be treated by spraying or even dipping the entire top portion of the young plant into the solution. Use half the normal label rate for the first application.

When they are housed in the greenhouse spray the plants every two weeks. Rotate from product to product with every bi-weekly application and have natural contact killer applications taking place in between each different product. For example, if you are using azadirachtin, pyrethrins, spinosad, and a natural contact killer, then a bi-weekly pest control program would go like this: contact killer > azadiratchtin > contact killer > pyrethrins > contact killer > spinosad > contact killer > azadirachtin, and so forth. The greenhouse environment is protected and the outdoor temperature may be cold enough that pests don't multiply, so using application rates that are half the normal use rate should be fine. After the plants are transplanted into their final outdoor containers start making weekly pest control applications using the same rotating technique described earlier. From the first pest control treatment up until the last, weekly or bi-weekly soil applications of beneficial microbes and compost teas should be used to re-fortify the rooting zone. This type of a weekly pest control program should keep any pest and insect populations to an absolute minimum. The programs should be performed until just before harvest. The products to be used should be low in oils, quick to naturally evaporate, and easily biodegradable so they won't leave a lasting residue. These characteristics, along with natural rains and rinsing off the crop with water a couple days before harvest, will help ensure that any traces of the natural and organic pest control products are eliminated from the plant surface before harvesting.

Chapter Eight

General Care & Maintenance for the Stages of Growth

A lot of information on how to grow a high performance outdoor cannabis garden has been presented. It is important to reinforce the fact that success is only achieved through not cutting corners and by paying close attention to every aspect of the garden. Treating each individual step with the same due diligence and importance as the others is the most reliable path to obtaining vigorous growth and impressive yields. This chapter provides a quick overview of the general care and maintenance during each of the developmental stages.

Propagation Stage

Propagation may be the shortest stage of development, but that in no way diminishes its importance. Cannabis plants that exhibit rapid growth above and below the soil should experience no disruption. Early stress induced by improper propagation techniques can result in slowed root growth throughout the vegetative growth stage leading to smaller plants. The key components to pay close attention to during propagation are temperature/humidity, watering, lighting, and timing.

The propagation stage will take around two weeks for seeds and an extra two to three weeks for clones, which allows them time to develop roots. For seeds, the first two days will be the germination period where they are soaked in a kelp and water solution. When it comes to clones the first two- to three-weeks will be required to initiate rooting. After the roots appear the plants will still need another two weeks to develop. Maintaining the proper temperature and humidity is extremely important for the entire time the plants are in the domed propagation tray. Temperatures between 70-80 degrees Fahrenheit with humidity levels between 60 to 70 percent work well for both seed germination and the rooting of cuttings. This will also keep the starter medium warm which encourages rapid root growth.

Along with a warm environment, the starter plants will require regular watering to maintain adequate moisture levels. The trick is to keep the growing medium consistently moist, but not soaking wet. When the medium is allowed to dry out too much the roots will begin to die back. Always use room temperature or slightly warmer water, and after each watering any excess water should be drained from the bottom of the tray. Watering each time with a light kelp and water solution will help the development of the root system. It will also provide a small amount of nutrition to the young, growing plants.

Propagation is best done indoors where conditions can be easily controlled and monitored. The domed tray containing the starter plants should be placed under a four-bulb t5 or t8 fluorescent grow-light fixture with the lights turned on for 18 hours a day. Hang the lighting fixture so that it sits about an inch from the top of the dome and can be easily moved up and down. This will allow easy access to the trays when watering. After about a week the plants will start to fill out the tray and dome. At this point the dome can be periodically removed daily and eventually be removed altogether. Start by removing the dome for an hour or two each day, and then add more time until the plants are acclimated to the conditions outside the dome.

Timing is an important aspect in propagation and throughout the season. Growing an outdoor cannabis garden requires meeting the timing of seasonal changes. So starting early is essential if you want to have a large, high-yielding plant by fall. Seeds

Allow the plant to grow into the support cage and trellising.

should be started in early-to mid-March and clones should be started two to three weeks earlier to allow the cuttings to take root. After about two weeks the starter plants will begin to crowd out the propagation tray and will need to be transplanted into their first Smart Pot. aeration container and placed into a heated greenhouse. Depending on the amount of space available, the first container size should be between five and 15 gallons in volume. At the time of transplant, treat the roots with supplemental beneficial microorganisms and water them in completely. This will conclude the first stage of development.

Vegetative Stage

The vegetative stage of development is split into two separate parts: the early/mid vegetative stage and the mid/late vegetative stage. The early vegetative stage begins when the plants are transplanted from the propagation tray and placed into the greenhouse. Depending on weather conditions, it usually starts at the end of March and lasts until late May or early June. This stage will encompass the entire time up until the plants are transplanted into their final outdoor locations, which marks the beginning of the mid/late vegetative stage. The mid/late vegetative stage continues until the plants begin to flower in August. The distinction between both stages can be made because the general care and maintenance is slightly altered once the plants move from inside a greenhouse to outside.

Early/Mid Vegetative Stage

In the early/mid vegetative stage the goal is to create a healthy, extensive root system. Starting on the first day inoculate the plants with beneficial microorganisms. It is mandatory to continue to inoculate with beneficial microorganisms on a bi-weekly schedule. Improper watering can slow down root growth, so only water the plants when the soil begins to dry out. Carefully stick your finger into the growing medium to at least the second knuckle and you will be able to feel if it is still moist. When the top of the medium is almost completely dry it is likely time to water. The frequency of the waterings will be determined by the composition of the growing medium and how quickly that medium dries out. When watering, be sure to thoroughly drench the entire container, allowing for a small amount of runoff from the bottom. Room temperature water, or slightly warmer, should always be used. Also, depending on the growing medium, while in the early/mid vegetative stage the plants may require a bit of nutrition. Feeding with a vegetative fertilizer formula at half strength every other week should help the young plants achieve their nutrient needs.

Environmental conditions are also a large factor in the early/mid vegetative stage of development. The temperature in the greenhouse should range between

70 to 80 degrees Fahrenheit during the day with the night time temperature not dropping below 60 degrees. This may require the use of supplemental heating, especially at night. Cannabis plants in the early vegetative stage can grow efficiently in relatively higher humidity levels. So a humidity level of around 50 percent is ideal as long as a fan is utilized to accommodate air flow. In order to simulate the longer daylight hours of spring, supplement lighting with t5 or t8 fluorescents in the morning and evening so the total light received per day is between 14 and 18 hours.

In this stage a simple form of the pest control program (discussed in the previous chapter) should be put into action. Apply the natural and organic pest control products in a rotating fashion with applications occurring every other week. If the greenhouse is kept clean, the plants should remain free of pests. The early/mid vegetative stage is also the time to start supporting the plants so they do not fall over. Place a simple bamboo stake that runs parallel to the stem and secure it in place with tomato clips that fasten lightly around the stem of the plant. Keeping the plants upright at all times will limit the amount of stress they endure and allow them to receive maximum amounts of light. When the weather outside is consistently above 60-65 degrees Fahrenheit at night, it will be time to transplant them into their final containers.

Mid/Late Vegetative Stage

The mid/late vegetative stage begins when the plants are transplanted into their final outdoor containers, typically in late May or early June. This portion of the vegetative growth stage will run until the plants begin to flower in August. The goal of the mid/late vegetative stage is to facilitate robust growth of both the roots and the top of the plant. The bigger the plant is allowed to grow in this stage,

The base of a plant with the interior leaves and branches removed. Removing interior foliage allows for good air flow.

the larger the flowers will be at harvest. A complete vegetative fertilizer regiment should be started on a weekly basis with regular applications of beneficial micro-organisms taking place on at least a bi-weekly schedule. Along with a complete fertilization regiment, full implementation of the weekly, rotating pest control program will also begin in this stage.

As the plants get larger in the early summer months their ability to consume nutrients and water also increases. Depending on the amount of rainfall, the containers may need to be watered as frequently as every other day. During each watering the entire container should be completely moistened with 10 to 20 percent of the water delivered being allowed to drain from the bottom of the container. This method has dual purposes. First, it ensures that the growing medium is completely watered. Second, it will help to flush out any residual fertilizer that was not taken into the plant, limiting the possibility of nutrient build up or lock out. Collecting and testing the EC/ppm levels of the runoff will help you to determine if the weekly fertilizer applications are too strong. If the reading is higher than the levels used to feed, then the application rate can be lowered slightly.

Plant support is another vital component of the mid/late vegetative stage since at this point the plants are getting large. This will include building the internal support system and beginning the external caging. The internal caging and support should be erected right after transplanting the plants into the final outdoor containers. The external caging should be built before the longest branches begin to surpass the boundaries of the container itself. It is important to have the external caging in place so the plant is allowed to easily grow into it and will not have to be carefully manipulated into the holes of the caging by hand. Doing this can injure or even break the branches. Building the external caging needs to begin in the later parts of the vegetative stage and should be fully established by early in the flowering cycle.

The upper portion of the plant with the interior foliage removed.

A topic that has not been discussed is the need for pruning or thinning of the growing plant. Start pruning and thinning the plants during the mid/late vegetative stage with the overall goal being to eliminate all of the stems and leaves that do not receive an adequate amount of sunlight. Any branches and leaves contained in the center or internal portion of the plant canopy should be carefully removed. Start by identifying the longest growing branches all around and on top of the plant canopy. These will be the branches that receive the most sunlight and will experience the best vegetative growth and flower development. Internodal shoots or branches will grow out from the V-shaped point where the larger branches meet the main plant stem. These growing shoots are referred to as   suckers   and they will not develop as well as the larger external branches. Sucker branches will also divert some plant nutrients away from the larger branches, hindering them from growing to their maximum potential. When done properly, a pruned and thinned outdoor cannabis plant should have a thick, lush canopy all around with the inside area, near the stem, being nearly empty or hollow. Grooming the plants in this fashion not only allows for all of the sunlight and nutrients to be directed to the largest growing parts of the plant, it also allows for exceptional air flow through

Trim away excess, interior leaves and branches.

the plant canopy. Proper air flow will prevent excess water and humidity from accumulating in the plant canopy, lowering the potential for outbreaks of powdery mildew or mold. Pruning and thinning the plants will be a continuous job through the mid/late vegetative and flower stages.

Flowering Stage

The flowering stage of development starts in August and continues for the remainder of the season until harvesting in October. The same watering practices utilized in the mid/late vegetative stage should be continued. Allocate sufficient water for a 10 to 20 percent runoff to help maintain a nutrient-balanced root zone. Switch the fertilizer regimen from the higher nitrogen vegetative products to products higher in phosphorus that are designated for increased flower production. Applications of beneficial microorganisms should continue on the same regular schedule as before. The weekly, rotating pest control program started in the vegetative stage should also be continued. Continue fertilizing up until one to two weeks before harvest, allowing for adequate water flushing of the growing medium and the removal of any excess fertilizer that may negatively affect the taste of the end product.

During the earlier part of the flowering stage the external caging will need to be completed. The flower buds will be increasing in size at this time. As they grow larger their weight will increase and proper support will be essential. Likewise, before the plants get too tall the final trellising will need to be installed on the upper portion of the caging and support system. This will keep the top branches of the plant canopy from drooping over and blocking the sunlight from reaching the growth on the lower part of the plant. Similar to the external caging, the final trellising must be in place before the growing branches reach that point. After the final trellising is finished and in place, the plant support system will be complete.

Pruning and thinning the plants will be a constant job throughout the flowering stage. Strive to maintain an internal plant canopy, near the stem, that is barren and allows for plenty of airflow. This is especially crucial during the flowering stage. Problems caused by high moisture levels, such as powdery mildew or mold, can cause severe damage to the developing buds and lead to a drop in yields. As the plants get closer to harvest, the larger fan or water leaves can also be removed. This will direct almost all of the plants energy and nutrient reserves straight to the growing buds. Do not remove the leaves that are higher up on the branches and closer to the flower buds. These will be needed to continue the process of photosynthesis and to maintain a higher metabolic rate within the plant.

Chapter Nine

Harvest

For the past eight or nine months you've been diligently tending to your crop and paying close attention to every last detail. The high-performance outdoor cannabis garden is now full of enormous plants with lush growth. The time to reap the fruits, or flowers, of your labor has finally arrived. You may feel like you have reached the finish line. Not so fast. There is more work to be done. The buds need to be harvested, trimmed, dried, and cured. Though this last portion of the job seems small when compared to the rest of the season, if it is not done properly the quality of the buds can be drastically diminished. Working hard all season only to end up with a mediocre product can be avoided if the same detail to attention that was given throughout the season is also given to the harvest. Harvesting at the right time and drying/curing the buds to perfection will help your product stand above the competition and give you the respect a worthy grower deserves.

A valuable practice to follow is flushing the growing medium for up to two weeks before the desired harvest date. Flushing entails feeding with only water and stopping the application of nutrients until harvest. Doing so allows the plant to absorb any remaining nutrients in the soil and to metabolize them so there are limited traces left in the harvested bud. This will ensure that the finished product is less harsh and has a natural flavor and aroma. As the soil nutrient levels decline the plant will begin to consume its own sugars and starches as a source of energy, which also results in a markedly better product. At the same time you start the flushing process you should also remove any remaining large fan leaves that will not be part of the final harvest. Doing so will make sure any remaining nutrients and plant energy will be directed to the actively growing flower buds, leading to an increase in their size. The question you may be asking yourself right now is this: If the growing medium should be flushed for up to two weeks before the projected harvest date, how do I know when the buds will be ready to be harvested? To know when to begin flushing you must be able to determine when the buds are ripe. Pinpointing when the buds are ripe is best done by utilizing a two-pronged approach.

Determining Ripeness

Not all of the buds will become ripe at the same time. You should understand that the quality is best when they are harvested at peak ripeness. The timing in which the buds are harvested will affect the appearance, aroma, flavor, and overall potency for the end user. Typically the window for harvesting is two to four weeks. Buds that are harvested too early will be relatively low in THC and have little effect on the end user. Buds picked at the beginning of the harvest window will contain more of the psychotropic cannabinoid THC (Delta9-Tetrahydrocannabinol) and will produce more of a clear-headed and uplifted feeling. The later the buds are harvested the more of a sedative-like effect they will have which is good for treating problems like insomnia. When the buds are allowed to ripen for

As a majority of the hair like structures called pistols begin to change from white to brownish red (color may differ by variety) the buds are nearing their peak point of maturity and are almost ready to harvest.

longer periods of time the THC will begin to degrade and convert into another cannabinoid called CBN (Cannabinol), which is responsible for the lazier, more relaxed sensation.

There are two main methods for determining when a bud is of peak ripeness. One way is by noticing the change of color and shape in the pistils of the flower. The pistils are the hairlike structures that protrude out from the flower itself. These are the part of the flower that catches pollen from a male flower to initiate fertilization and seed formation. Since all of the plants should be females there will not be any cross pollination and those pistils can be used to determine the stage of ripening.

Early on in the flowers development the pistils, or hairs, " will be white in color and stick pretty much straight out. This is the plant attempting to collect as much pollen as possible, which it will be unable to do. As the flowers begin to ripen the pistils will start changing from white to a brownish orange or golden color. This signifies that the plant is beginning to ramp up the production of THC. As the

Depending on the desired effect of the finished product, trichomes can be allowed to continue their color change until they reach an almost amber shade.

color of the pistils change they will also start to curl in closer to the flower itself. For a product that is higher in THC, that offers the clear headed feeling, the buds should be harvested when 40 to 60 percent of the pistils, or hairs, have changed in color. The remaining white pistils will continue changing color during the drying process. Harvesting within this time period will almost always ensure a high quality yield. After 70 to 90 percent of the pistils, or hairs, are allowed to change color they will become darker brown or red. At this time the levels of THC will be lower with higher levels of the CBN cannabinoid that causes the sedative affect. The exact colors of the pistils may vary from strain to strain, but the overall concept for determining ripeness remains the same.

The other way of visually determining a buds state of ripeness is through close inspection of the trichomes that inhabit the leaves surrounding the flower. Trichomes are tiny glandular structures that grow from the surface of the leaves and give the buds their crystal-like appearance. They are comprised of a stem with a little bulb on top and kind of resemble tiny mushrooms. Cannabinoids, such as THC and other essential oils or terpenes, are created and stored within the tips of the trichomes. Their main purpose from an evolutionary point of view is to protect the plant from the suns UV rays and external attacks by insects and other pests. Trichomes can also help a grower determine when the bud is reaching a desired stage of ripeness.

As was the case with the pistils of the flower, trichomes can tell us quite a bit just by their appearance alone. In the early stages of flower production the trichomes begin to develop. They initially look clear and glasslike, but as the bud begins to ripen they also begin to change. The first change they make is a transitioning from a clear state to one that is cloudier or opaque. At this stage the trichomes are producing higher amounts of THC and offer more of a psychotropic effect. When 80 to 90 percent of the trichomes become cloudy and opaque, the buds are at maximum quality and should be harvested. After the trichomes reach the cloudy stage their color will shift yet again to more of an amber color. At this, and subsequent stages, the THC will start breaking down and converting to CBN giving the product more of a sedative (couch lock) quality. For best results, unless you want a higher CBN product, be sure to harvest before five to 10 percent of the trichomes turn amber in color. As was the case with the flower pistils, the trichome color changes may differ for each individual strain but the initial transition to cloudy will be similar. Since trichomes are quite small, a magnification instrument should be used to appropriately judge their appearance.

Multiple Cut Harvest

Buds grown in a high-performance outdoor cannabis garden are similar to tomatoes in the sense that they will not all ripen at the same time. When growing large cannabis plants, which have several flowering points, the top parts of the canopy that receive the most sunlight will ripen first, followed closely by the surrounding lower branches. For this reason, the tops of the plant should be harvested first. Harvesting the upper branches first also allows more sunlight to reach the lower branches. This increased exposure to sunlight reduces the time it takes for them to ripen. If you wait to harvest until the lower branches are ready, then the top buds will become overripe and the quality will decrease.

In the early part of the harvest window, when the buds on the top of the canopy are ready, harvest them using large pruning shears that can easily cut through the stems. The stems can be thick, therefore long-handled pruning shears like the ones used to prune bushes and small tree branches work best. Harvest by cutting the branches from the plant about four- to six-inches below the bottom-most flower bud on the stem. If possible, make the cut just below the point of another lateral shoot that connects to the main stem. This should create a V that will also be a handy way to hang the buds to dry. Immediately after cutting off the branch remove, by hand, any remaining larger fan or sugar leaves as these are no longer needed. When they are ready and ripe, lower branches should be harvested in the same fashion. Depending on the size of the plant, it may take up to four separate harvest cuts spread out over a week or so to gather the entire crop. The best time to harvest is in the morning or early evening when the rate of photosynthesis is lower and the plants are not creating as many sugars and starches that can negatively affect the quality. After the stems, full of buds, are harvested it is time to dry and trim them down.

Trimming and Work Force

The choice of whether to trim the harvested buds before or after drying them is up to you as a grower. Both methods come with their own sets of ups and downs. Harvesting when the product is still wet, before drying, is often the easier choice but it can affect flavor in the end. When wet leaves are cut back the chlorophyll that is still somewhat fresh can leach back into the stem and relocate into the flowers. This may result in the buds having a slight grassy or hay-type taste to them. Allowing the buds to properly dry before trimming will give the remaining chlorophyll molecules time to breakdown or degrade to where they will no longer affect the taste. Trimming the buds after drying is more difficult than doing so when they are fresh. As the leaves dry they have a tendency to curl back and around the buds making them harder to trim. If great care is not given when trimming dry buds the end product can become overly leafy.

When trimming wet or fresh cannabis you will want to cut back the leaves that are protruding past the flower. Cut the leaves back so they are flush with the bud itself, giving the finished product a nice uniform appearance. If the leaves are coated by heavy trichome production you may want to trim a little less and keep more of the leaf. The remaining leaf will curl around the flower as it dries, which can add to the bud's aesthetic appeal. Dry buds should be trimmed in the same fashion. Though it may be a bit more difficult, having the leaves in place when the bud is dried will help the trimmer identify how much of each leaf to remove and how much to leave intact. Regardless of whether the trimming is to be done wet or dry, it is best to use handheld precision trimmers. Do not use electronic trimming machines. The shape, size, and design of electric trimmers may vary but, for the most part, they all come with the same major disadvantage of trimming too closely to the bud itself. The goal when trimming is to remove the larger leafy matter so the flower buds have a more uniform look that is not stringy with dried leaves. Electric trimmers tend to cut so close that they damage the actual bud, resulting in a noticeable drop in the weight of the overall yield, especially if you had a large harvest. Trimming by hand may take longer but the accuracy of each deliberate cut is significantly increased.

Proper trimming takes a great deal of time. Depending on the number of plants and their size, trimming all of them by hand can be a monumental undertaking. For example, if you grow 25 plants and yield 10 pounds per plant there will be 250 pounds that need to be carefully manicured. Doing so alone would take far too long since the key to trimming the crop is to get it done in the least amount of time as possible. Hiring outside help is the best way to get the job done quickly and more efficiently. In places like the Emerald Triangle in California there are seasonal workers that specialize in trimming. They start showing up in the area as harvest time grows near. These workers have been aptly referred to as trimmigrants and many are very skilled at the job.

Trimming is a slow and tedious process and the best trimmers can only trim somewhere around a pound every four hours. If you find someone that can average two pounds a day, keep them around because they are a golden asset. When hiring outside help, try to find trustworthy people that are hardworking and reliable and not someone that hangs out and admires the crop all day. You want someone that is there to get the job done. With that said, it is important to provide any workers with a fair wage for their work. If you are unsure of how much to compensate them, then ask other growers to see what the prevailing wage is for your area. Also, before hiring any trimmers do the right thing and review any rules and regulations to make sure you do so legally.

Before trimming begins, be sure that you have enough trimming supplies like precision trimmers and heavy-duty latex gloves. Make sure to keep the cutting blades of the precision trimmers cleaned and lubricated. The buds contain lots of resins that will collect on the tools and hands (hence the gloves). Clean the trimming blades often with isopropyl alcohol, which sterilizes them as well. To avoid unwanted chemicals, choose a lubricant that is labeled as food-grade safe to keep the tools operating. Additionally, be sure to save all of the trim that is removed because it can be used to make one of the many popular cannabis by-products that are helping to fuel the market. The array of by-products is vast and includes items such as extracts, hash, oils, salves, shatter, wax, edibles, topical creams, and even lip balm.

Drying

Drying is the first step in the preservation of the harvest. The goal is to remove most of the remaining moisture from the buds so they will taste and burn better. The moisture needs to be drawn out at a nice slow pace so the buds dry evenly but do not become overly dry and begin to crumble. This should take five to 10 days, depending on the relative humidity levels in the drying room. Ideally, the

Harvested buds should be hung to dry in a dark room that is relatively cool and dry. Fans can be used to provide adequate air flow around the buds to evenly distribute any remaining moisture.

drying area should be cool, dark, and dry with a relative humidity between 30 to 50 percent. If the relative humidity rises above 50 percent, incorporating a de-humidifier into the drying room is a simple solution. For the best results, the temperature should remain between 70-75 degrees Fahrenheit. Depending on the weather in the fall, the temperatures may reach closer to 80 degrees Fahrenheit. This should not cause any issues as long as the room stays dry. Try to avoid using an air conditioner because they can cause the buds to dry too quickly. A fan should be used to keep air flowing around the buds and help keep the temperature and moisture levels even throughout the room. Run the fan on low or medium and aim it towards a nearby wall to deflect and circulate the air. Aiming the fan directly at the buds will certainly dry them too fast.

To start drying the harvest, run string horizontally at about eye level. Use heavy-duty string so to ensure it won't snap or break from the weight of the buds. Hang the flower branches from the string so that the buds are pointing towards the ground. The branches that were cut at a point where another lateral stem creates a V shape can be hung by resting the center of the V on to the string. They should balance well enough so they won't fall. Straight branches that do not have the V can be hung with the help of clothes pins or similar style clips. When hanging the buds to dry, make sure to leave a few inches of space between the separate branches so they do not touch each other and the air can easily flow around them. Doing so will allow them to dry more evenly and at a uniform pace. Another important thing to do is to space the drying strings far enough away from each other so there is enough space to walk between them and monitor the drying process.

The drying buds should be checked at least once a day to see how they are progressing and to make sure you catch them before they get too dry. The best way to assess the progress of the drying buds is by hand. When the buds are properly dried the outside will appear completely dry but the insides will still be sort of squishy or soft. This means there is still a moderate amount of moisture on the internal portion of the bud. During the curing process this moisture will become evenly distributed among the buds, leaving them not overly moist or overly dry. When the buds are done drying the smallest stems should snap when bent and the large stems should bend but not easily break. If the buds are dried for too long THC can begin to break down and degrade into CBN. When the buds are dried too fast they may become brittle and crumble when touched. This is why paying close attention to the temperature and humidity conditions in the room is so important. Improperly drying the buds can have a noticeable and negative effect on their overall quality.

Curing

Curing is a technique growers use to help preserve the cannabis harvests for longer periods of time by allowing the remaining moisture within the buds to become more evenly distributed. At the same time, curing also allows for the continued break down, or degradation, of the chlorophyll molecules within the leaves and buds. Buds that retain higher levels of chlorophyll tend to have a harsher taste when smoked. Large scale commercial cannabis operations often skip the curing process and sell the crop after just drying alone. They do this in an effort to achieve a quicker return on investment. With no curing, however, cannabis is less flavorful, less aromatic, and will not maintain freshness and quality over time. Cannabis that has been thoroughly cured and properly stored can last up to a year without a noticeable decline in quality.

The curing process should begin immediately following the drying stage. Taking the time to properly cure your harvest will create a high quality product that reflects your hard work. This could take two to three months so patience is indeed a virtue. The wait will surely be worth it.

To properly execute the curing process you will need some type of airtight container. Harvests from a high-performance outdoor cannabis garden tend to be quite plentiful so large plastic tote containers are often the best choice. Buds can be cured while still attached to the main stem but they will take up more space and require the use of several containers. In an effort to limit the amount of curing containers needed the individual buds should be removed from the main stem beforehand. This is referred to as bucking it down and will make the curing process a bit easier to handle.

After the buds are properly dried they will need to be carefully trimmed and stored for the curing process.

Fill each large plastic container about 80 percent full of the buds and immediately close the lid securely. Not filling the containers all the way ensures that fresh air can be exchanged for the moisture-laden air from within. For the first four- to five-weeks of curing the lids should be removed once a day to release the moisture and allow more fresh air in. When the lid is open it is also good practice to stir the buds so they can cure evenly. This prevents the buds on the bottom from sitting in higher moisture levels than the top ones. Doing this also helps eliminate the possibility of mold growth on the buds. The ideal relative humidity within the containers is 50 to 60 percent. External hygrometers with wired or wireless sensors are a handy way to monitor this. If the humidity level is too high then the buds were not dried long enough and should be removed from the container for a day or so. After a month or so you should be able to stop removing the lid daily; check them every two to four days instead. When the moisture levels are evenly distributed throughout the buds the curing process is complete. To check this, gently squeeze the buds between your fingers. If the buds feel evenly dry and do not crumble from the touch, then they are ready for blending and long term storage. If the buds feel too dry they may have been cured too long. Most grow stores will have some type of humidity-supplying pack that can be placed in the container for a couple days to help replenish the moisture within the buds.

Blending Of Finished Product & Long Term Storage

Curing the buds is the best way to achieve an even consistency of moisture and dryness within the buds, but since they are several different sizes they will need to be mixed together properly. Blending the finished product ensures the packaged product will equally represent all of the different individual buds. In each individual package, blend together equal amounts of the big, mid-sized, and small buds to create a nice even mix. If some of the smaller buds ended up a little dryer than the bigger ones they too will benefit from product blending as they will gather some moisture from the larger buds, improving their quality.

Harvested buds drying in a repurposed shipping container with an industrial dehumidifier for maintaining a proper level of humidity.

When deciding which container to use for storing the product, the first thing to do is determine how long the product will need to be stored. If you plan on selling it into the medical market within one- to two-months the storage container can be different than if you plan on holding it for six to eight months, or even a year. For shorter term storage standard turkey bags that don t allow air in or out, and will maintain freshness, are price effective and work great. For longer term storage, wide-mouthed glass mason jars are a good choice, but if the harvest is a big one it will take a lot of jars to contain it. Vacuum-sealed bags will give you excellent long-term storage capabilities and can hold more product comparatively. There are even devices on the market today that add nitrogen as a gas into the bag while it is being sealed. This helps maintain optimal freshness for longer periods of time while not affecting flavor, and is the same process used to bag potato chips. When stored in a completely airtight container the high-performance outdoor cannabis crop can last for up to a year without losing much of its flavor and potency. After the buds have been placed and sealed in their storage container they should be kept in a cool, dark place that can be easily monitored until they are sold.

When a mature plant is ready for harvest the first cuts should be made to the top portion of the plant. These areas receive the most sunlight and will be ready to pick first. Subsequent cuts should be made as the remaining buds reach the desired level of maturity.

Chapter Ten

Marketing the Product

The final step with your garden is properly marketing and selling the finished product. You need to obtain a substantial return on investment. The return will vary depending on the size of the garden, but the cost of supplies, production, maintenance, and labor can be substantial. The good news is that if everything up to this point was done correctly you should have an exceptional harvest of high-quality cannabis and recouping the loss of initial investment should not be a problem. Making a profit will ensure the operation is sustainable for years to come. The real question is how big of a profit can one achieve.

When marketing and selling your product it is a great idea to have a plan in place before the harvest. There may be more than one outlet you can utilize for getting the product into the marketplace. These include facilities such as medical dispensaries or patient cooperatives and clubs. Directly networking with the managers or purchasers at the licensed facilities near you can help establish a professional business relationship and a possible destination for your product. Focus on doing business with people whom you can trust to treat you and your brand with the same respect and dignity that they would like in return. When everything is done with mutual respect and professionalism your business operations should go smoothly.

Before selling any of the crop into the marketplace, make sure to thoroughly review all of the state, county, and local laws and regulations that pertain to the sale and distribution of cannabis. Having a high-performance outdoor cannabis garden that is sustainable from year to year requires the operator to stay within the confines of the law. Remaining compliant is the safest way to stay in business and to limit the stress that can come from being in an industry that is still somewhat on the fringe, at least with regards to federal law.

> *"Consider the season when selling your product"*

Have a clear understanding of how and where it is acceptable to sell the product well before you begin to market. Be aware that laws and regulations can change from county to county and even within different municipalities. What may be legal in your area could very well not be legal in the next city or county. In some cases it may be legal to sell the product, but illegal to transport it. This is one of the gray areas in many of the numerous medical cannabis laws throughout the country. For example, currently the California Highway Patrol follows federal cannabis guidelines and considers the plant a Schedule 1 drug that has no medicinal properties. This means they still consider the plant to be illegal. If they catch someone transporting product within their jurisdiction they will confiscate the crop and prosecute the offender to the furthest extent of the law. This can and does happen even though the cannabis was grown in a legal manner. This may seem unfair but it is the result of a state law directly contradicting its federal counterpart.

Transportation of your product is important. I use a trusted driver to deliver and do not make deliveries myself. Payment is almost always made before delivery. Obviously the driver will need to obey all traffic laws and store the product in an inconspicuous location in his vehicle.

Carefully reviewing and understanding the laws that govern your state and local area is the best way to avoid any trouble. If you do choose to distribute your product on the black market or over state lines, then remember that if you get caught you could lose everything you have worked for and possibly be incarcerated.

Consider the season when selling your product. Cannabis has become a real commodity so you will have countless competitors. Prices will fluctuate based on supply and demand. Be patient and learn when to sell in order to achieve the best returns. In general, demand is relatively constant, leaving supply as a guiding factor. In the winter, just after harvest, the price will be lower compared to spring and summer. Selling your product when the market is overly saturated with competition will result in a lower profit margin. Being patient and allowing the price to rise again will allow you to get a better return on your investment.

Seasonal marketing highlights the importance of properly curing and storing your crop so it can maintain its quality for up to a year. If it is still moist and not cured well, or stored in an area that is too warm, the quality of the cannabis can degrade within just a couple months. Since there is heavy competition, purchasers want to buy from those who can regularly supply a high quality product that is free of chemical pesticides. Your goal should be to supply their needs for as much of the year as possible. Also, keep in mind that you are not only marketing the product, you are marketing yourself as well. Always take care to provide a superior product that will set you apart from the others. This leads to satisfied customers who regard you as a grower to be trusted and someone with whom they will continue to do business.

Competition in the cannabis market is fierce. Take pride in your garden. Not cutting corners will help you remain a relevant fixture in the market place.

Chapter Eleven

Conclusion

A successful high-performance outdoor cannabis garden is ultimately the sum of all its parts. When each aspect of the method outlined within this book is given the utmost dedication and attention, the end result will be a garden of tall, bulky plants with high-quality yields. Lack of devotion to the task will bring diminished results. It is important to follow through and execute each phase of the process without cutting corners. Don t be lazy. A performance garden starts with a sizable investment of time and money relative to the gardens size. But when done properly the benefits are great and well worth the effort.

The days of outdoor-grown cannabis being inferior to its indoor counterpart are over. Through specific breeding and selection, cannabis strains tailored for outdoor growing can yield a crop that is extremely high in both quality and appearance. Growing a strain that has been proven by growers to be reliable time and time again will give you a successful harvest. Take special care in selecting a strain to grow and make sure the crop receives everything it needs.

Keep in mind that the crop you are growing is ultimately intended for human ingestion. For many people cannabis is a medicine that benefits their lives. Harmful chemical pesticides should be avoided completely. Medicines are meant to help. The addition of chemicals that can cause serious health issues shows bad judgment on the growers behalf. Using natural and organic methods to control pests and disease, as outlined here, is an effective way to protect both your crop and those who consume it. Whether you are growing for the recreational or medicinal market, it is important to produce product that is safe for the end user.

Growing medicinal or recreational cannabis can be a lucrative business. If you would like to continue doing so year after year, stay within the law. Read and understand all of the laws and regulations from the state, county, and local municipalities that pertain to outdoor cannabis production. Having a strong understanding of the legalities surrounding your operation allows you to operate legally and helps guide your business decisions. Not having a clear understanding of the laws or choosing to ignore them can result in the loss of your garden and possible incarceration. Following all of the laws and regulations is the only way to ensure that your operation can grow and be sustainable for seasons to come.

Remember that the Performance Gardening method is scalable to size and will work for all outdoor growers. It is adaptable to any outdoor cannabis garden regardless of how much space is available and how many plants are grown, whether its 100 plants or just 10, or 1,000-gallon containers or 200 gallon. Plants grown in a high-performance outdoor cannabis garden are allowed to reach their full genetic potential and will grant the grower tremendous yields. Growing cannabis indoors is rife with limitations, but outdoors: the sky is the limit!

A great grower never stops learning. In horticulture, you can always learn something new.